Jim Snidero

The Essence Of Bebop
Piano & Guitar

advance music | improvisation

Jim Snidero

The Essence Of Bebop Piano & Guitar

10 great studies in the style and language of bebop

ADV 14116

www.advancemusic.com | © 2021 advance music GmbH, Mainz | Printed in Germany

Translation: Lindsay Chalmers-Gerbracht
Editing (German): Julia Baldauf
Cover design: Elke Dörr
Music engraving: Annette Vosteen
Layout and typesetting: Waldemar Klein (Werbestudio Klein, Mainz)
All historic photographs by William P. Gottlieb. Source/Credit Line:
William P. Gottlieb/Ira and Leonore S. Gershwin Fund Collection,
Music Division, Library of Congress.

© 2021 advance music GmbH, Mainz, Germany

ADV 14116
ISBN 978-3-95481-075-8
ISMN 979-0-2063-0356-2

Table of Contents | Inhaltsverzeichnis

	Page | Seite	Listening Track With Soloist | Vollversion	Play-Along Track Rhythm Section Only | Play-Along-Track
Foreword & Acknowledgements | Vorwort & Danksagung	7		
Study Guide Overview | Studienleitfaden	9		
Style | Stilfragen	12		
Tuning Concert A | Stimmton A (klingend)		1	
Tuning Concert B♭ | Stimmton B♭ (klingend)		2	
1. Monktified	14	3	15
2. The Messengers	18	4	16
3. Amazing Bud	22	5	17
4. Pure Silver	26	6	18
5. Miles '63	30	7	19
6. Bird And Diz	35	8	20
7. Straight Trane	40	9	21
8. Freddie	45	10|11	22|23
9. One For Sonny	50	12	24
10. Bird	55	13|14	25|26

APPENDIX | ANHANG

Interview: Ken Peplowski On Studying With Sonny Stitt |
Interview mit Ken Peplowski über das Studium bei Sonny Stitt .. 61

Suggested Reading | Literaturempfehlungen 62

Suggested Listening & Videos | Hörempfehlungen und Videos 63

About The Author And The Musicians |
Über den Autor und die Musiker 64

Audio Track Personnel
Anders Bostrom – Flute
Mike LeDonne – Piano
Peter Washington – Double Bass
Joe Farnsworth – Drums

Recording Engineer – Michael Brorby
Recorded Dec 9– 20, 2019, at Acoustic Recording, Brooklyn, New York
Mastering Engineer – Peter Karl
Produced by Jim Snidero

Downloading The Audio Tracks | Zum Audio-Track-Download

Please visit www.schott-music.com/online-material to download the audio tracks using the following voucher code: 6H3Mw8Dv

Bitte besuchen Sie die Website www.schott-music.com/online-material und laden Sie die Audio-Tracks mit dem folgenden Gutscheincode kostenlos herunter: 6H3Mw8Dv

Foreword & Acknowledgements

It would be difficult to overstate the influence of bebop on the music we listen to today. Developed in New York by a handful of brilliant African-American musicians in the 1940's, bebop took jazz off the dance floor, introducing fast tempos, advancements in harmony, rhythm and melody that are the bedrock of modern music. The astonishing artistry and virtuosity during the bebop era significantly raised the bar for improvising musicians worldwide, and is the inspiration for *The Essence Of Bebop*.

I've spent a large part of my life studying and playing bebop and hard-bop, so it's not something I take lightly. Bebop is the foundation of who I am as a jazz musician. The goal here is to demonstrate specific techniques invented and/or developed by a few key figures in the bebop and hard-bop eras that influenced the music. Since these eras include many incredible artists and a vast number of recordings, it's obviously impossible to cover everything in ten etudes, hence the title of the book. But there should be enough to provide a solid foundation to better understand bebop and hard-bop.

Unquestionably, Charlie "Bird" Parker was the most influential musician of the bebop era. His concepts were used by virtually every bebop and hard-bop artist, and are prevalent throughout this book. Bud Powell, Dizzy Gillespie and Thelonious Monk are the other "pure" bebop artists, while Miles Davis, Sonny Rollins, Art Blakey and Horace Silver began as bebop artists, then became leaders of the hard-bop movement and beyond.

Concepts within *The Messengers* and *Pure Silver* etudes include some members of Blakey's and Silver's hard-bop groups, specifically Hank Mobley, Lee Morgan and Blue Mitchell. John Coltrane and Freddie Hubbard both became jazz icons during the hard-bop era, with Coltrane becoming a hugely important innovator. *Miles '63* is the latest chronologically, essentially a link between hard-bop and 20th century classical music.

These ten etudes loosely progress in difficulty, with the two fastest tempos (*Freddie* and *Bird*) towards the end of the book. Level of difficulty is also relative to the various instrument editions. Generally, they will be more difficult for brass players than woodwind players, but as the accompanying audio tracks demonstrate, they can be played well, and sound very good, on any of these instruments.

We have provided a list of recordings/videos that contain the original compositions used as inspiration for this book. In order to have any chance of mastering bebop, it's vital that you spend a lot of time listening to, really living with, recordings of the masters. I believe these etudes are valuable, but they're really just an introduction to their music. I

Vorwort & Danksagung

Man kann den Einfluss des Bebop auf die heutige Musik kaum überbewerten. Von einer Handvoll brillanter afroamerikanischer Musiker im New York der 1940er-Jahre entwickelt, löste der Bebop den Jazz von der Tanzfläche und bereicherte ihn mit schnellen Tempi sowie harmonischen, rhythmischen und melodischen Weiterentwicklungen, die zu Fundamenten der modernen Musik geworden sind. Die erstaunliche Kunstfertigkeit und Virtuosität der Bebop-Ära stellten deutlich höhere Ansprüche an improvisierende Musiker auf der ganzen Welt und lieferten schließlich die Inspiration für das Heft *The Essence Of Bebop*.

Ich habe einen Großteil meines Lebens mit dem Studium und dem Spielen von Bebop und Hardbop verbracht; diese Musikstile haben daher eine entscheidende Rolle in meinem Leben gespielt und Bebop bildet einen Grundstein meiner Persönlichkeit als Jazzmusiker. Das Ziel dieses Heftes ist es, bestimmte Techniken aufzuzeigen, die von einigen Schlüsselfiguren des Bebop und Hardbop erfunden und/oder entwickelt wurden und die Musik beeinflusst haben. Da diese Ära zahlreiche unglaublich gute Musiker und eine riesige Anzahl von Aufnahmen hervorgebracht hat, ist es natürlich unmöglich, alles in (nur) zehn Lektionen vorzustellen. Das Heft enthält aber reichlich Material für ein besseres Verständnis des Bebop und Hardbop.

Charlie "Bird" Parker war ohne Zweifel der einflussreichste Musiker der Bebop-Ära; seine Konzepte wurden von fast jedem Bebop- und Hardbop-Künstler aufgegriffen und tauchen daher immer wieder im ganzen Heft auf. Auch Bud Powell, Dizzy Gillespie und Thelonious Monk gehören zu den ‚reinen' Bebop-Musikern, während Miles Davis, Sonny Rollins, Art Blakey und Horace Silver als Bebop-Künstler begannen, bevor sie zu führenden Figuren des Hardbop wurden.

Die Etüden *The Messengers* und *Pure Silver* gehen teilweise auf Konzepte von einigen Mitgliedern der Hardbop-Gruppen von Blakey und Silver zurück, darunter insbesondere Ideen von Hank Mobley, Lee Morgan und Blue Mitchell. John Coltrane und Freddie Hubbard avancierten beide zu Jazz-Ikonen der Bebop-Ära und Coltrane machte sich einen Namen als maßgeblicher Innovator. Chronologisch gesehen ist *Miles '63* das jüngste der Stücke und stellt eine Verbindung von Hardbop und der klassischen Musik des 20. Jahrhunderts dar.

Die zehn Etüden steigern sich allmählich im Schwierigkeitsgrad, die Stücke im schnellsten Tempo (*Freddie* und *Bird*) erscheinen gegen Ende des Bandes. Der Schwierigkeitsgrad fällt bei den verschiedenen Instrumentalausgaben unterschiedlich aus; generell sind die Stücke auf einem Blechblasinstrument etwas schwerer zu spielen als auf einem Holzblasinstrument. Wie auf den Audio-Tracks zu hö-

suggest that you transcribe heads, arrangements and solos to build your knowledge and instrumental ability, play along with the recordings and play what you've learned with other musicians.

Finally, I'd like to thank all of the musicians that performed on the recordings included in this series. They are all virtuoso artists of the highest order, and important figures in jazz history. In my opinion, their incredible performances on these play-alongs do justice to the artists that were the inspiration for this book. I am both humbled and honored to call them my friends and colleagues.

Jim Snidero

ren ist, klingen die Etüden auf allen Instrumenten gut und sind durchaus spielbar.

Wir haben eine Liste der Aufnahmen/Videos der Originalkompositionen, die für das vorliegende Heft als Quelle der Inspiration gedient haben, zusammengestellt. Um Bebop überhaupt zu meistern, sollten Sie viel Zeit in das Hören der Aufnahmen der Meister investieren, ja sozusagen auch damit leben. Die Etüden sind gewiss wertvoll, bieten aber lediglich eine Einführung in diese Musik. Mein Vorschlag wäre, dass Sie Ihr Wissen und Ihr instrumentales Können steigern, indem Sie Heads (Themenköpfe), Arrangements und Soli transkribieren, zu den Aufnahmen mitspielen und alles, was Sie neu gelernt haben, auch mit anderen Musikern zusammen spielen.

Schließlich möchte ich mich bei allen Musikern, die bei den Aufnahmen zu dieser Serie mitgewirkt haben, bedanken. Sie sind ausnahmslos virtuose Künstler ersten Ranges und dazu noch wichtige Persönlichkeiten der Jazzgeschichte. Meines Erachtens werden diese Aufnahmen denjenigen Künstlern, welche die Inspiration zu diesem Band gegeben haben, gerecht. Es ist mir eine große Ehre, sie zu meinen Freunden und Kollegen zu zählen.

Jim Snidero

Study Guide Overview

Each etude has an accompanying study guide that provides historical background, jazz theory, solo concepts and practice suggestions. Though a lot can be learned from simply practicing the etudes, these study guides will give you a deeper understanding that can potentially form the basis for informed jazz improvisation.

The 10 etudes included here are based on the most common **forms** in bebop; AABA, AA', blues and rhythm changes. There are other forms, but this covers the vast majority in bebop.

As discussed in the interview section, bebop masters considered II-V-I to be the predominant **chord progression** of this era. There are literally hundreds of **II-V-Is**, and their variations, in these etudes, much of which is discussed in the study guides, including major and minor II-V-I, II7-V-I, III-VI-II-V-I, tritone substitutes, minor IV-♭VII, chromatic substitutions, altered and diminished V7.

Scale theory and chord/scale relationships include major, melodic minor, harmonic minor, diminished, altered, whole tone, bebop scales and dominant bebop, adding half steps between second and root and sixth and fifth, and modes.

Beyond scales, an analysis of **melodic techniques** explores symmetrical and asymmetrical phrasing, enclosures, scale/arpeggio combinations, melodic shapes and links, passing tones, guide tones, side-stepping and quotes.

Finally, some attention has been given to the often-overlooked subject of **solo construction**. Timing, pacing, balance and the solo arc all help to put melody, harmony and rhythm in context, giving a solo flow, logic and drama.

Included are a few **exercises** that will help in understanding chords and scales, as well as a few vocabulary studies to demonstrate ways of integrating the material, but there are many more possibilities. For example, one of the most common techniques jazz improvisors use to master chord changes and vocabulary (including greats like George Coleman) is to practice them in every key. It could be as simple as example 1 in *Monktified*, which is a dominant 7 riff around the circle of fourths, or a II-V-I idea such as example 13 in *Miles '63*. Perhaps a little more challenging would be example 17 in *Bird And Diz*, a I-V-I exercise, and yet more challenging, practicing a chorus or more of *Bird* in every key. There's really no limit to how exercises can be constructed, so use your imagination.

Studienleitfaden

Jede Etüde wird von einem Studienleitfaden ergänzt, der einen historischen Abriss des Stückes, Jazztheorie, Solokonzepte und Übe-Tipps enthält. Auch wenn man beim Üben der Etüden viel lernen kann, bietet der Studienleitfaden ein tieferes Verständnis der Musik, das eine mögliche Grundlage für informierte Jazzimprovisation sein kann.

Die zehn Etüden im Heft basieren auf den am häufigsten verwendeten **Songformen** im Bebop: AABA, AA', Blues und Rhythm Changes. Auch wenn weitere Formen vorkommen können, so decken diese bereits die überwiegende Mehrzahl der im Bebop verwendeten Formen ab.

Wie im Interview am Ende der Ausgabe erwähnt, betrachteten die Meister des Bebop die II-V-I-Verbindung als die vorherrschende **Akkordprogression** in dieser Zeit. Es kommen in der Tat Hunderte Arten der **II-V-I** mit Variationen bei diesen Etüden vor; in den Studienleitfäden werden viele davon erläutert, darunter II-V-I in Dur und Moll, II7-V-I, III-VI-II-V-I, Tritonussubstitutionen, IV-♭VII in Moll, chromatische Substitutionen, alterierte und verminderte V7-Akkorde.

Aus dem Bereich der **Akkord-Skalen-Theorie** kommen hier folgende Themen zur Sprache: Durtonleitern, melodische und harmonische Molltonleitern, verminderte, alterierte und Ganztonleitern, Bebopskalen und Dominant-Bebopskalen, sowie Erweiterungen mit Halbtonschritten zwischen der zweiten Stufe und dem Grundton und zwischen der sechsten und fünften Stufe, und auch Kirchentonleitern.

Eine Analyse der weiteren **melodischen Techniken** untersucht symmetrische und asymmetrische Phrasierung, Umspielungen, Skalen-/Arpeggien-Kombinationen, melodische Konturen und Verbindungen, Durchgangsnoten, Guide Tones (Leittöne), Rückungen und Zitate.

Schließlich wird auch das meist wenig beachtete Thema **Konstruktion eines Solos** behandelt. Timing, Pacing (der Wechsel von dichten und weniger dichten Passagen), Balance und Soloaufbau unterstützen den melodischen, harmonischen und rhythmischen Kontext eines Solos, damit es fließt und sowohl Logik als auch Drama enthält.

Einige **Übungen** sollen das Verständnis für Akkorde und Skalen erleichtern; Vokabular-Studien zeigen einige Beispiele, wie man das Material in eigene Improvisationen integrieren kann, auch wenn die Möglichkeiten eigentlich unbegrenzt sind. Eine der häufigsten von Jazz-Improvisatoren angewendeten Techniken, um Akkordverbindungen und Vokabular zu meistern (sogar Jazz-Größen wie George Coleman), ist das Üben in allen Tonarten. Eine ganz einfache Methode (Beispiel 1 bei *Monktified*) ist ein Dominantsept-Riff im Quartenzirkel oder ein II-V-I-Lick wie in Beispiel 13 bei *Miles '63*. Eine etwas größere Herausforderung wäre Beispiel 17 zu *Bird And Diz*, eine I-V-I-Übung, und, noch etwas anspruchsvoller, das Üben eines oder mehrerer Chorusse aus *Bird* in allen Tonarten. Da dem Erfinden von Übungen keine Grenzen gesetzt sind, können Sie gerne Ihre Vorstellungskraft voll ausschöpfen.

Study Guide Subjects

1. Monktified
- Blues form
- Dominant 7 riff
- Circle of fourths
- Major II-V-I
- Flat 5 on V7
- 2-measure phrasing
- Whole-tone scale
- Awareness of beat 1

2. The Messengers
- AABA form
- Development of blues ideas
- Minor II-V-I
- Solo balance with blues and changes
- Harmonic and melodic minor scales
- Double time

3. Amazing Bud
- Enclosures
- Syncopation
- Major bebop scale
- Solo balance with diatonic melodies and changes
- Tritone substitution

4. Pure Silver
- AA' form
- Swing eighth notes
- Major 7 on dominant 7 chord
- Altered V7
- Dominant bebop scale
- Mode relationship between Dorian and Mixolydian (IIm7-V7)
- Melodic links

5. Miles '63
- Rests and phrasing
- Diminished chord, whole-half diminished scale
- Triplets
- Chord extensions and bitonality
- V7 chord, half-whole diminished scale
- 4-measure turnaround
- Pacing and the solo arc
- Adding a chromatic note between the second and the root on a dominant bebop scale

Themen des Studienleitfadens

1. Monktified
- Blues-Form
- Riff auf Dominantseptakkord
- Quartenzirkel
- II-V-I in Dur
- Verminderte Quinte auf V7-Akkord
- Zweitaktige Phrasierung
- Ganztonleiter
- Wahrnehmung von Schlag „1"

2. The Messengers
- AABA-Form
- Blues-Ideen entwickeln
- II-V-I in Moll
- Ein ausgewogenes Solo schaffen mithilfe von Blues und Akkordfolgen
- Harmonische und melodische Molltonleiter
- Double-Time

3. Amazing Bud
- Umspielungen
- Synkopen
- Bebopskala in Dur
- Ein ausgewogenes Solo schaffen mithilfe von diatonischen Melodien und Akkordfolgen
- Tritonussubstitution

4. Pure Silver
- AA'-Form
- Swing-Achtelnoten
- Große Septime auf Dominantseptakkord
- Alterierte V7-Akkorde
- Dominant-Bebopskala
- Modalbeziehung zwischen dorisch und mixolydisch (IIm7-V7)
- Einzeltöne als Verbindung zwischen Akkorden

5. Miles '63
- Pausen und Phrasierung
- Verminderte Akkorde und Ganzton-Halbton-Skala
- Triolen
- Akkorderweiterungen und Bitonalität
- V7-Akkord und Halbton-Ganztonleiter
- 4-taktiger Turnaround
- Pacing und der Aufbau eines Solos
- Zusatz einer chromatischen Note zwischen der zweiten Stufe und dem Grundton bei der Dominant-Bebopskala

6. Bird And Diz
- Mode relationship between Dorian and Locrian (IIm7 and VIIm7♭5)
- Balancing syncopation
- Leading tones on downbeats
- V7 color variations
- Other uses of blues ideas
- Major II-V in a minor key

7. Straight Trane
- Intensive study in II-Vs
- 1-measure II-Vs down in whole steps
- 2-measure phrasing concepts
- Color options on minor II-Vs
- Major and minor II-V7 relationship

8. Freddie
- Feeling fast tempos
- Lines on fast tempos
- Rests on fast tempos
- Tritone II-V
- Adding a chromatic note from the sixth on a dominant bebop scale
- 2-measure turnaround
- Song-like melodies

9. One For Sonny
- Musicality on a ballad
- Enhancing the melody
- Turnaround substitutions
- Chromatically descending II-Vs
- IVm-♭VII progression
- Chromatically side-stepping

10. Bird
- Rhythm changes
- Diatonic melodies
- Ebb and flow
- Asymmetrical phrasing
- Substitutions
- Quotes

6. Bird And Diz
- Modalbeziehung zwischen dorisch und lokrisch (IIm7 und VIIm7♭5)
- Synkopen
- Leittöne auf Grundschlägen
- V7-Farbvariationen
- Weitere Anwendungen von Blues-Licks
- Dur-II-V in einer Molltonart

7. Straight Trane
- Intensive II-V-Studien
- II-V mit halbtaktigen Akkordwechseln in Ganztonschritten abwärts
- 2-taktige Phrasierungskonzepte
- Farboptionen bei II-V in Moll
- Die II-V7-Verbindung in Dur und Moll

8. Freddie
- Gefühl für schnelle Tempi
- Linien bei schnellen Tempi
- Pausen bei schnellen Tempi
- Tritonus-II-V
- Zusatz einer chromatischen Note zwischen sechster und fünfter Stufe bei der Dominant-Bebopskala
- 2-taktiger Turnaround
- gesangliche Melodien

9. One For Sonny
- Musikalität beim Balladenstil
- Verzieren der Melodie
- Substitutionen beim Turnaround
- Chromatisch absteigende II-V
- IVm-♭VII-Verbindung
- Chromatische Rückungen

10. Bird
- Rhythm Changes
- Diatonische Melodien
- Fließendes Spielen
- Asymmetrische Phrasierung
- Substitutionen
- Zitate

Style

Piano Intro

Bud Powell's Bebop piano style involves "shell voicings" – left hand plays roots with guide tones (7th and 3rd), spanning a seventh (1-7 or 1-♭7) or a tenth (1-♭7-♭3 or 1-♭7-3 or 1-7-3). However, when playing bebop or hard bop, contemporary pianists rarely play roots unless there's no bassist. Another option is to play roots short, while holding on to guide tones, like drummers feathering the bass drum so it's barely heard.

There are many materials available on piano chord voicings, but there are two basic ii/V7/I voicings for LH comping while playing lines in RH, using good voice leading:

ii7 (♭3-♭7-9), V7 (♭7-3-13), I (3-7-9)
and
ii7 (♭7-♭3-5), V7 (3-♭7-9), I (7-3-5)

When both hands comp, avoid note doubling by using "drop-2" voicings.

"Voicings" concern arrangement of a chord's notes. Piano "voicing" also means playing notes louder or softer than others in a chord, requiring finger control with proper weight distribution in hand and wrist – i.e., fingers close to keyboard, attentive to notes' sonorous inter-relationships, eliciting different colors, nuances, and harmonic clarity.

When listening to/watching Bud Powell play (e.g., "I Want to Be Happy" 1961 in Paris), his touch is light, relaxed, his fingers never raised high, enabling maximum control of dynamics, phrasing, and articulation.

Students are taught to change the "damper" pedal when harmonies change, but I advise using it mainly for harmonic embellishment, avoiding it for melodic material; instead of relying on the pedal to sustain notes, use finger legato.

For comping, pianists often use variations of the Charleston rhythm (dotted quarter, followed by an eighth note), starting on downbeats or upbeats anywhere in a measure. Articulate using long-short, short-long, short-short, or long-long combinations.

Luke Gillespie

Stilfragen

Klavier Intro

Bud Powells Klavierstil beim Bebop ist gekennzeichnet durch „Shell-Voicings" [zweistimmige Begleitung in der LH i. d. R. mit Terz und Septim], bei der die linke Hand Grundtöne mit Leittönen (Septen und Terzen) spielt, die das Intervall eines Septen (1-7 oder 1-♭7) oder Dezimen (1-♭7-♭3 oder 1-♭7-3 oder 1-7-3) umspannen. Allerdings spielen moderne Pianisten selten Grundtöne in Bebop oder Hardbop, es sei denn, es ist kein Bassist dabei. Als weitere Option kann man kurze Grundtöne spielen, während man die Leittöne lange aushält, etwa wie Schlagzeuger die große Trommel ‚federn', damit sie kaum wahrnehmbar ist.

Es gibt viele Möglichkeiten, Akkord-Voicings [akkordische Begleitung in der LH] auf dem Klavier zu realisieren. Zwei gute ii/V7/I Grund-Voicings für die Begleitung in der LH bei gleichzeitigem Spielen der Melodielinie in der RH, die zur guten Stimmführung führen sind: ii7 (♭3-♭7-9), V7 (♭7-3-13), I (3-7-9) oder ii7 (♭7-♭3-5), V7 (3-♭7-9), I (7-3-5). Bei Akkord-Begleitungen mit beiden Händen kann man eine Verdopplung der Noten durch „drop-2"-Voicings vermeiden.

Der Begriff „Voicings" bezieht sich auf die Verteilung der Noten im Akkord. Darüber hinaus bedeutet „Voicing" in Bezug auf das Klavier das Herausheben bestimmter Töne im Akkord, die etwas lauter oder leiser als die anderen gespielt werden. Dafür benötigt man ein besonderes Fingerspitzengefühl bei der korrekten Gewichtsverteilung der Hände und Handgelenke, d.h. die Finger sind eng an der Tastatur zu halten und große Aufmerksamkeit bei verschiedenen klanglichen Zusammenhängen auszuüben, um dem Klavier verschiedene Tonfärbung, Nuancierungen und harmonische Klarheit zu entlocken.

Wenn man Bud Powell beim Spielen zuschaut oder zuhört (z.B. „I Want to Be Happy" 1961 in Paris), erkennt man, dass er mit sehr leichtem Anschlag spielt und die Finger immer eng an der Tastatur hält, um durchgehend die größtmögliche Kontrolle über Dynamik, Phrasierung und Artikulation zu halten.

Studenten wird beigebracht, das Dämpferpedal bei einer Harmoniewechsel zu betätigen. Ich rate aber eher dazu, dieses Pedal hauptsächlich für harmonische Verzierung zu nehmen und nicht für melodisches Material. Es ist günstiger, Finger-Legato anzuwenden anstatt Töne mit dem Pedal zu verlängern.

Pianisten setzen häufig auf Variationen der Charleston-Rhythmen (punktierte Viertelnote plus Achtelnote) als Begleitung, indem sie auf geraden oder ungeraden Schlägen irgendwo im Takt beginnen. Am besten sind kombinierte Artikulationen, wie zum Beispiel lang-kurz, kurz-lang, kurz-kurz oder lang-lang.

Luke Gillespie

Guitar Intro

Guitar music sounds an octave lower than written. (So middle C is written in the staff for guitar.) If the music is not written for the guitar, then adjust accordingly. First thing I do when reading music is to look at the range of the music. For instance, if I see a high C above the staff then I will play in the middle of the neck 8th position to avoid hand position jumps.

Phrasing: As guitarists there are many picking techniques and picking every note can make the line dig in and swing harder. However, it is sometimes good to use occasional pull-offs and hammer-ons when you see a slur or can hear it in the phrase to avoid picking every note. This makes the line smoother and less like a trumpet or tenor sax player tonguing every note.

When playing in a trio situation it sounds good to comp at times when playing a melody and during a solo similar to a pianist's left hand. (If there is a pianist comping it is best to use this idea sparingly to avoid clashing with piano and cluttering up the music).

A good default rhythm in jazz for the guitar is called the "Charleston Rhythm" (Quarter note, eight rest, half note tied to eight note). If you are playing a line and there is a measure rest you might only punch a chord on the 2nd note (as in bars 4, 8, and 12 of the melody of *Monktified*).

It is sometimes possible to play a chord voicing right on beat 1 and play the melodic line if the line is within the chord on the guitar, especially on melodies, (but this would be something that you might have to work out after becoming more familiar with the music).

Dave Stryker

Gitarre Intro

Auf der Gitarre spielt man eine Oktave tiefer als notiert (C4 steht also in Gitarrenmusik auf dem zweiten Zwischenraum von oben). Sollte die Musik nicht speziell für Gitarre geschrieben sein, muss man entsprechend oktavieren. Beim ersten Blick in die Noten ist es ratsam, die Stimmlage des ganzen Stückes zu etablieren. Wenn ich zum Beispiel ein hohes C oberhalb der Notenlinien sehe, spiele ich dann in der 8. Lage mitten im Gitarrenhals, um große Lagenwechselsprünge zu vermeiden.

Phrasierung: Gitarristen verfügen über viele Picking-Techniken: Das Picken jeder Note gibt der Linie mehr Tiefe und einen größeren Schwung. Von Zeit zu Zeit ist es aber gut, bei Legato-Bögen Pull-Offs und Hammer-Ons einzusetzen, um das Picken jeder Note zeitweise zu unterbrechen. Die Linie klingt dadurch „smooth" und vermeidet den Eindruck, als ob Trompeter oder Tenorsaxophonisten Zungenschläge auf jedem Ton spielen würden.

Beim Triospiel ist das zeitweilige „Comping" [d. h. Begleiten] bei der Melodie oder in Solos wie in der linken Hand des Pianisten schon vorteilhaft. (Sollte der Pianist aber auch Comping anwenden, ist es besser, weniger Begleitfiguren zu spielen, um Kollisionen mit dem Pianisten und das Überladen der Musik zu vermeiden).

Ein beliebter Standardrhythmus beim Jazzgitarrenspiel heißt „Charleston-Rhythmus" (Viertelnote, Achtelpause, Halbe Note mit Achtelnote gebunden). Wenn du eine Linie mit einer Ganztaktpause spielst, könntest du eventuell lediglich auf der zweiten Note einen Akkord anschlagen (wie in T. 4, 8, und 12 in der Melodie „Monktified").

Es ist mitunter möglich, ein Akkord-Voicing [akkordische Begleitung] direkt auf den 1. Schlag zu platzieren und die melodische Linie dann zu spielen, falls sie innerhalb des Gitarren-Akkords fällt (das sollte man aber erst herausarbeiten, wenn man das Stück sehr gut kennt).

Dave Stryker

52nd Street, New York, N.Y., ca. July 1948

1. Monktified

Jim Snidero

© 2021 advance music GmbH, Mainz | ADV 14116

*) GT = guide tone PT = passing tone / Durchgangston LT = leading tone / Leitton / Annäherung

Das widerrechtliche Kopieren von Noten ist gesetzlich verboten und kann privat- und strafrechtlich verfolgt werden.
Unauthorised copying of music is forbidden by law, and may result in criminal or civil action.

Monktified

As the house pianist at *Minton's Playhouse* in the early to mid 1940's, Thelonious Monk was at the forefront of the bebop movement. One of the most distinct styles to emerge in the bebop era, Monk favored an angular melodic approach, plenty of space and a percussive attack. He recorded his tune *Blue Monk* the most, a blues in his favorite key of concert B♭, which is what *Monktified* is based on.

A blues form is almost always 12 measures (ms) when played in 4/4. It is often conceived as having three 4-measure sections, basically a beginning, middle and end. In this version of the blues, the last 4-measure section uses the chord progression II-V-I, the most important progression in bebop.

1. The head, chorus 4 and chorus 5 contain riffs, which are melodic phrases that are repeated to build intensity or contrast with lines. Since riffs are usually short and fairly simple, they are ideal to practice in different keys. Chorus 5 uses a riff that emphasizes the fundamental notes of a dominant 7 chord (1, 3, 5, ♭7), providing a solid, earthy feeling. (Monk would often play repeated notes short.) This could be practiced on any dominant 7 chord progression, but two common ones are up in half steps and the circle of fourths.

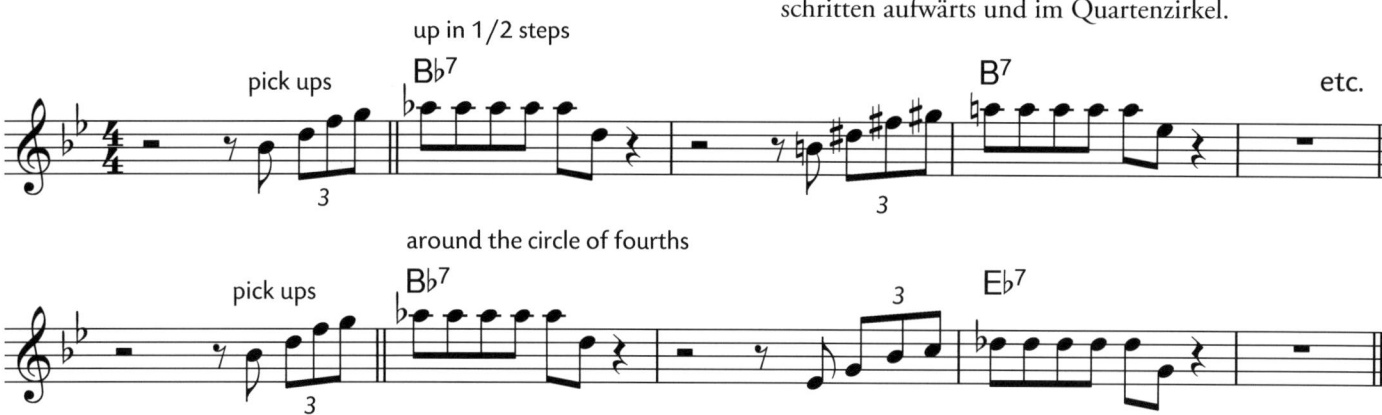

It's important to hear this riff as a pickup into a 2-ms phrase, as this is a natural way to group ideas together and usually aligns with chord progressions (e.g. symmetrical phrasing).

2. Riffs in ms 1–8 on the head and chorus 4 emphasize extensions of the dominant chord. The colors of extensions have the effect of a floating or hovering feeling, as opposed to fundamental tones, which sound more stable. Practicing these riffs in different keys will help you to become more familiar with extensions.

3. Bebop musicians liked to emphasize the flat 5 on dominant 7 chords, which can sound a bit mysterious or surprising. Measures 9 and 10 of the head set up, then sustain, the flat 5 for 3 beats, resolving to the riff. The last note of ms 17 emphasizes the flat 5 on E♭7.

4. The mostly diatonic line in ms 33–35 uses guide tones to "sound the changes" (imply the chord progression) on a major II-V-I.

T. 9 und 10 wird die erniedrigte Quinte zunächst etabliert und dann für drei Schläge gehalten, woraufhin sie sich in den Anfang des Riffs auflöst. Die letzte Note in T. 17 betont die erniedrigte Quinte auf E♭7.

4. Die überwiegend diatonische Linie in T. 33–35 verwendet Guide-Tones, um die Akkorde einer II-V-I in Dur auszuspielen (die Akkordfolge anzudeuten).

5. Monk probably used the whole tone scale more than any other bebop musician (ms 22–23), which has a unique, floating character.
6. In ms 46–48, a 4-beat line is played on beat 1, then repeated again but on beat 2, creating the illusion of a shifting meter. Monk uses the same technique on *Blue Monk*. Practice ms 45–48 while counting 1-2-3-4 in your head. Always be aware of where beat 1 falls, and try to hear the off-set line against 4/4. This will help you develop an overall better sense of time.

5. Monk verwendete die Ganztonleiter vermutlich häufiger als alle anderen Bebop-Musiker (T. 22–23): Sie hat einen unverwechselbaren, schwebenden Charakter.
6. In T. 46–48 wird eine eintaktige Linie beginnend auf dem ersten Schlag gespielt, dann im nächsten Takt wiederholt, dort aber auf dem zweiten Schlag beginnend, was einen Taktwechsel vortäuscht. Die gleiche Technik wird von Monk in *Blue Monk* verwendet. Wenn Sie T. 45–48 üben, sollten Sie 1-2-3-4 im Kopf zählen. Vergewissern Sie sich, wo der erste Schlag jeweils fällt und versuchen Sie, die verschobene Linie gegen den 4/4-Takt zu hören. Dadurch werden Sie ein besseres Gefühl für die *time* entwickeln (*time*: Zeitgefühl, Puls, auch Timing).

Portrait of Thelonious Monk, Minton's Playhouse, New York, N.Y., ca. Sept. 1947

2. The Messengers

Jim Snidero

▶ TRACK 4/16

© 2021 advance music GmbH, Mainz

*) GT = guide tone PT = passing tone / Durchgangston LT = leading tone / Leitton, Annäherung

The Messengers

Originally formed along with Horace Silver, Art Blakey was most associated with *The Jazz Messengers*, leading the group for about 35 years from 1955 to 1990. Art Blakey is considered the father of hard bop, and *The Jazz Messengers* the first hard bop group, launching the careers of many influential jazz figures including Hank Mobley, Lee Morgan, Wayne Shorter, Cedar Walton and Freddie Hubbard, among others.

Hard bop musicians often used arrangements to present their music in a more organized manner than bebop jam sessions, and incorporated elements of gospel, R & B, and blues. *The Messengers* is based on *Moanin'*, an archetypical tune of the hard bop era composed by Jazz Messenger pianist Bobby Timmons.

1. The 32-measure form of *The Messengers* is AABA, the most common in jazz. During the head the rhythm section repeats the "amen" IV-I chord progression on the A sections, introducing gospel into the arrangement. During the solo section, the A sections then repeat a series of 4 chords; Fm-A♭^{7}-G$^{7♭9}$-C^{7}alt (Im-♭III7-II7-V7). Alternate notes have been provided during the double-time passages.
2. The bridge provides a temporary relief from the A section, briefly going to B♭ minor (IVm) twice before heading back to F minor (Im). However, the melody is exclusively based on the F minor blues scale, giving the bridge continuity with the A section.
3. Surprisingly, F blues-type ideas work over the four repeated chords on the A section. Hard bop musicians used a lot of blues ideas, and could play them in any key. There are many blues-type ideas in this etude to help build your vocabulary. It would be a great idea to learn some of them in all keys.
4. The first chorus is inspired by the great trumpet player Lee Morgan, who was a master of this blues/gospel-type tune. One technique he used was to state an idea, then develop it over about four measures. This happens in the first four measures of each A section of the first chorus.

The Messengers

Zusammen mit Horace Silver war Art Blakey eines der Gründungsmitglieder der Gruppe *The Jazz Messengers* und war 35 Jahre lang der Leiter des Ensembles, zwischen 1955 und 1990. Art Blakey wird als Vater des Hardbop angesehen und *The Jazz Messengers* war die früheste Hardbop-Gruppe, die für die Karrieren vieler einflussreicher Jazzmusiker, darunter Hank Mobley, Lee Morgan, Wayne Shorter, Cedar Walton und Freddie Hubbard, maßgeblich war.

Hardbop-Musiker präsentierten ihre Musik in Form von festgelegten Arrangements und hoben sich dadurch von den üblichen informellen Jam-Sessions des Bebop ab. Dabei integrierten sie Elemente von Gospel, R & B und Blues. *The Messengers* basiert auf *Moanin'*, einer archetypischen Melodie der Hardbop-Ära, die vom Jazz-Messenger-Pianist Bobby Timmons komponiert wurde.

1. Das 32-taktige Stück *The Messengers* ist in AABA-Form geschrieben, der gängigsten Form im Jazz. Beim Thema wiederholt die Rhythmusgruppe die „Amen"-Kadenz IV-I in den A-Teilen, die einen Hauch von Gospel in die Musik bringt. In den A-Teilen des Soloabschnitts werden die vier Akkorde Fm-A♭^{7}-G$^{7♭9}$-C^{7}alt (Im-♭III7-II7-V7) wiederholt. Für die Double-Time-Passagen ist eine vereinfachte Fassung angegeben.
2. Die Bridge (Überleitung, auch „B-Teil"; Anm. d. Red.) löst den A-Teil mit zwei kurzen Ausflügen nach B♭-Moll (IVm) ab, bevor sie nach F-Moll (Im) zurückkehrt. Die Melodie aber beruht ausschließlich auf der F-Moll-Bluestonleiter, wodurch Bridge und A-Teil auch hörbar eine Einheit bilden.
3. Überraschenderweise funktionieren Blues-Ideen in F über die vier Akkorde des A-Teils sehr gut. Hardbop-Musiker machten ausgiebig Gebrauch von Blues-Licks und spielten sie in allen Tonarten. Diese Etüde enthält viele Blues-Ideen, die Ihr musikalisches Vokabular bereichern könnten. Es wäre auch vorteilhaft, wenn Sie einige davon in allen Tonarten üben könnten.
4. Der erste Chorus ist von dem großen Trompeter Lee Morgan inspiriert, einem Meister der Blues- und gospelartigen Melodien. Eine seiner Techniken bestand darin, eine Idee vorzustellen und anschließend über etwa vier Takte zu entwickeln. Auf diese Weise sind auch die ersten vier Takte der A-Teile im ersten Chorus angelegt.

5. Hard bop musicians still used sophisticated bebop language, often to contrast the earthiness of the blues. The trick is finding a balance between the two languages. One common technique is using a II-V-I idea (in this case, mostly minor II-V-Is with a flat 5 on II) here and there to create tension and release (ms 40–42, 45–46, 50–52, 65–66).

5. Hardbop-Musiker verwendeten weiterhin die komplexe Sprache des Bebop, häufig als Kontrast zum erdigen Klang des Blues. Die Kunst besteht darin, eine Balance zwischen den zwei Idiomen zu finden. So kann man zum Beispiel gelegentlich ein Kadenz-Idee einstreuen (hier wäre dies eine II-V-I in Moll, mit verminderter Quinte auf II), um Spannung und Entspannung zu erzeugen (T. 40–42, 45–46, 50–52, 65–66).

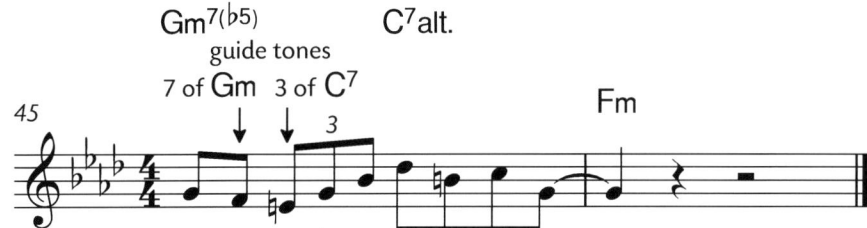

6. Another way to create contrast to the blues is using ideas based on other scales. The ideas in ms 60–63 are based on the F melodic minor scale, and the double-time idea in measure 71 is based on the F harmonic minor scale.
7. Double time creates excitement and showcases technical abilities. In ms 67–71, four short double-time phrases sound the changes with ms 67–68 and 71 using a classic melodic shape of gradual 'up and down', then quick 'up'. Though double time can be played anywhere in a solo, timing is important. This particular solo builds intensity, saving double time until the end of the solo, with a long rest setting up the double-time passage.

6. Man kann aber auch mithilfe von anderen Tonleitern Kontraste zum Blues erzeugen: T. 60–63 basieren auf F melodisch Moll, die Double-Time-Idee in T. 71 auf F harmonisch Moll.
7. Double-Time-Passagen erzeugen Spannung und demonstrieren technische Finesse. Die Akkorde in T. 67–71 werden in vier kurzen Double-Time-Phrasen ausgespielt, wobei T. 67–68 und T. 71 einem typischen melodischen Pattern folgen: eine allmählich aufsteigende, dann absteigende Linie, gefolgt von einem schnellen aufsteigenden Lauf. Auch wenn man Double-Time grundsätzlich in allen Abschnitten eines Solos einsetzen kann, sollte man den Spannungsbogen im Blick haben. In diesem Solo wird zuerst die Intensität aufgebaut, bevor Double-Time erst am Ende des Soloabschnitts, nach einer längeren Pause, eingesetzt wird.

3. Amazing Bud

Jim Snidero

♩ = 149

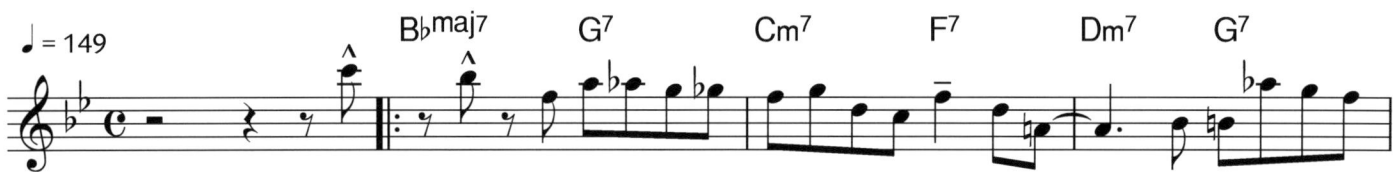
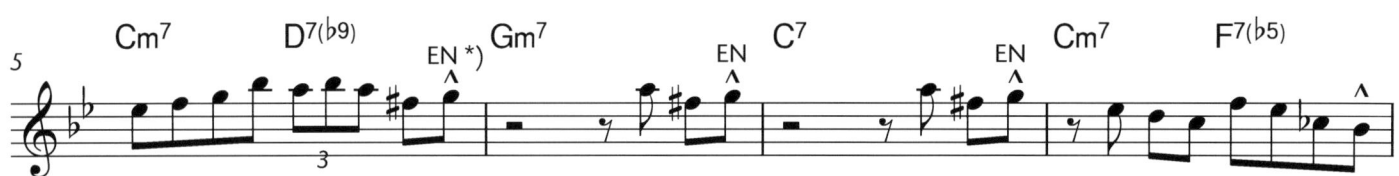

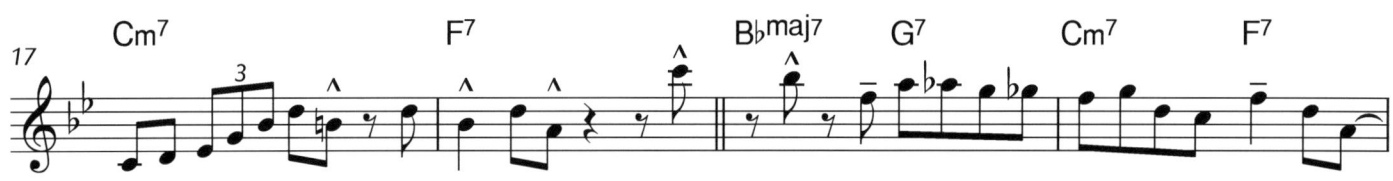

*) EN = enclosed note / umspielter Ton GT = guide tone PT = passing tone / Durchgangston LT = leading tone / Leitton / Annäherung

Amazing Bud

Bud Powell was the first to successfully adopt Charlie Parker's concepts on the piano, and one of the few bebop musicians to equal Bird's technical brilliance. Bud is considered the foundation of modern jazz piano, influencing many historical figures including Horace Silver, Wynton Kelly, Herbie Hancock and Chick Corea, to name just a few.

1. *Amazing Bud* is the first 'classic' bebop etude in this collection, and is based on Bud's composition *Bouncing With Bud,* first recorded with Sonny Rollins and Fats Navarro in 1949. In concert B♭, it has a 32-measure AABA form, with the bridge going to the relative minor of concert G.
2. One of the main characteristics of jazz in general, and bebop in particular, is the use of syncopation, which helps energizes the music and most importantly, swing. Syncopation can be created by up-beat (also known as weak beat) rhythms, but it can also be implied by emphasizing up beats in an eighth-note line, using a direction change or ending on an up beat.

   The first four measures are a good example of how a combination of syncopated rhythms and lines creates a phrase that swings.
3. Bud used a lot of enclosures, which is a melodic technique of approaching a note from both sides with either a half or whole step. Enclosed notes are indicated with EN (only the first time in repeated lines). Here's a good exercise that encloses notes of a major triad:

4. The idea in ms 28 is based on the major bebop scale, adding a half step between 5 and 6 of the B♭ major scale. Adding this half step places notes of the major triad on downbeats, helping the line to sound the changes. Bebop scales are usually played descending, and are often followed by an arpeggio ascending.

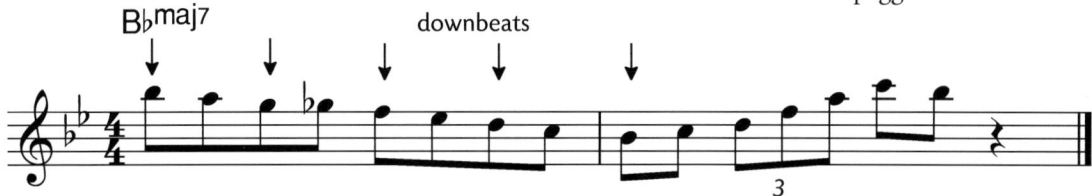

Amazing Bud

Bud Powell war der erste, der die Konzepte von Charlie Parker auf dem Klavier erfolgreich umsetzte, und auch einer der wenigen Bebop-Musiker, die mit Birds technischer Brillanz gleichziehen konnten. Bud wird als der Begründer des modernen Jazz-Pianos betrachtet und beeinflusste viele historische Persönlichkeiten des Jazz, wie z. B. Horace Silver, Wynton Kelly, Herbie Hancock und Chick Corea, um nur einige zu nennen.

1. *Amazing Bud* ist die erste klassische Bebop-Etüde dieser Sammlung und basiert auf Buds Komposition *Bouncing With Bud*, die mit Sonny Rollins und Fats Navarro 1949 erstmalig aufgenommen wurde. Das Stück hat eine Länge von 32 Takten, folgt der AABA-Form und steht in klingend B♭-Dur, wobei die Bridge in die parallele Molltonart klingend G-Moll moduliert.
2. Synkopen sind generell ein Hauptmerkmal des Jazz und ein spezieller Bestandteil von Bebop. Sie bringen Energie in die Musik und vor allem Swing. Synkopen kann man durch das Spielen von Rhythmen auf „und"-Zählzeiten erzeugen, oder indem man die Offbeats in einer Achtelnotenlinie betont; das geschieht durch Richtungswechsel oder das Beenden der Phrase auf dem Offbeat.

   Wie man eine swingende Phrase durch die Kombination von synkopierten Rhythmen und Linien kreiert, zeigen die ersten vier Takte im Stück.
3. Bud verwendete häufig Umspielungen, hierbei wird ein Melodieton in Halb- oder Ganztonschritten von oben und unten „umkreist". Umspielungen werden hier durch die Abkürzung EN markiert (lediglich beim ersten Auftreten in wiederholten Linien). Nachfolgend finden Sie eine schöne Übung für die Umspielung der Töne in einem Dur-Dreiklang:

4. Die Idee in T. 28 basiert auf der Bebop-Durtonleiter, die einen zusätzlichen Halbton zwischen der 5. und 6. Note enthält (Ton G♭ in B♭-Dur). Durch diesen zusätzlichen Halbtonschritt erklingen die Töne des Dur-Dreiklangs auf dem Schlag, dadurch wird der Akkord durch die Linie schön verdeutlicht. Üblicherweise wird die Bebop-Tonleiter abwärts gespielt, gefolgt von einem aufsteigenden Arpeggio.

5. Though there are quite a few chords in this tune, they all basically function in the key of B♭ major. Similar to hard bop musicians balancing the blues with bebop language (e.g. *The Messengers*), bebop musicians were skilled at creating a balance between diatonic melodies and sounding the changes. Too many diatonic melodies can sound boring or old-fashioned, while too many changes can sound mechanical or academic.

   A classic way of balancing diatonic and 'sounding the changes'-type melodies on tunes cycling through I(or III)-VI-II-V, including rhythm changes, is to use diatonic melodies in ms 1–2, then changes in ms 3–4, creating the effect of harmonic tranquility followed by tension and release. This occurs on the first four measures of every A section in *Amazing Bud*.

6. On a V7 chord, bebop musicians often used the chord a tritone away to create tension, called a 'tritone substitution'. In ms 29 the chord is G^7, but the line implies D♭^{7}. Here's a simplified version of the line on six II-Vs descending in whole steps. Try practicing in the other six keys as well.

5. Obwohl dieses Stück eine Menge verschiedener Harmonien enthält, funktionieren alle grundsätzlich in B♭-Dur. Genau wie Hardbop-Musiker den Blues mit Bebop-Vokabeln ausbalancierten (z. B. *The Messengers*), konnten Bebop-Musiker sehr geschickt diatonische Melodien und akkordbezogene Patterns im Gleichgewicht halten. Ein Übermaß an diatonischen Melodien kann langweilig oder altmodisch klingen, während zu viele Akkordbrechungen mechanisch oder akademisch wirken können.

   In Stücken, die sich durch I (oder III)-VI-II-V bewegen (auch Rhythm Changes), wird ein Gleichgewicht zwischen Diatonik und akkordbezogenen Patterns klassischerweise wie folgt hergestellt: In Takt 1–2 spielt man eine diatonische Melodie, in Takt 3–4 spielt man die Akkorde aus. Dadurch erzeugt man abwechselnd Ruhe und das Gefühl von Spannung und Entspannung. Ein treffendes Beispiel findet man in den ersten vier Takten aller A-Teile in *Amazing Bud*.

6. Bebop-Musiker haben auf V7-Akkorde oft die sogenannte „Tritonussubstitution" angewendet: Auf einem V7-Akkord wird der Akkord im Tritonusabstand angedeutet, um Spannung zu erzeugen. Hier in T. 29 steht ein G^7-Akkord, die Linie suggeriert aber D♭^{7}. Im folgenden Beispiel finden Sie eine vereinfachte Version dieser Linie über sechs II-V-Verbindungen in Ganztönen abwärts. Versuchen Sie, das Beispiel auch in den anderen sechs Tonarten zu üben.

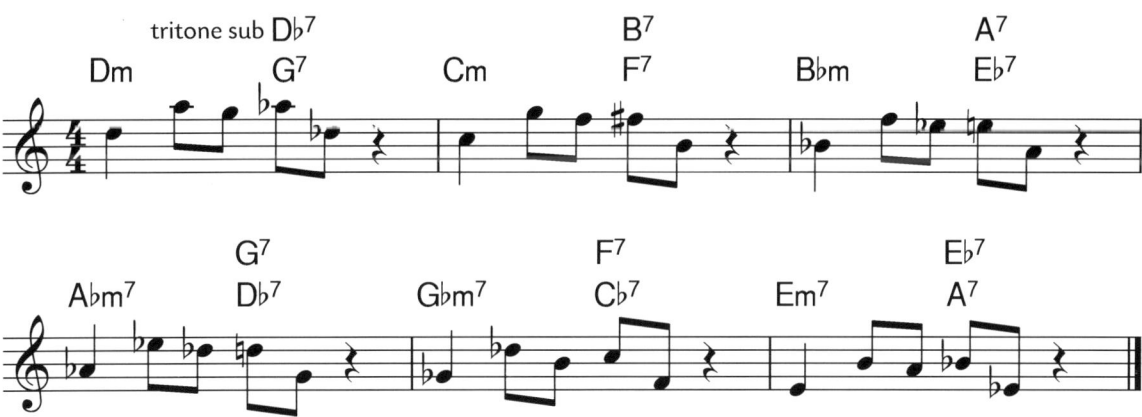

4. Pure Silver

Jim Snidero

© 2021 advance music GmbH, Mainz

*) EN = enclosed note / umspielter Ton GT = guide tone PT = passing tone / Durchgangston LT = leading tone / Leitton / Annäherung

Pure Silver

Although Horace Silver was an influential pianist (e. g. Mc-Coy Tyner, Herbie Hancock, etc.) his biggest contribution to jazz was that of a hard bop leader and composer. Many great players were members of his quintet, including Hank Mobley, Blue Mitchell, Louis Hayes, Joe Henderson, Woody Shaw, the Brecker Brothers and Tom Harrell, among others.

Horace was a prolific composer and arranger, and some of his tunes, such as *Song For My Father, Nica's Dream* and *Peace,* have become jazz standards. Horace had a very lyrical composing style which he often combined with interesting harmonies and chord changes.

1. *Pure Silver* is based on Horace's tune *Strollin'* and has a form of AA'. It's in concert D♭, which has a warm sound, but can have some technical challenges, and the tempo is one of the more difficult to play with a relaxed and swinging feel. However, don't confuse relaxed with a lazy feel, which can drag and lack energy. A great example is Blue Mitchell's playing on the original recording *Horace-Scope*. Relaxed, yet precise and energized.
   Alternate notes have been provided during the double-time passages.
2. The phrase in ms 53–55 is a good one to practice for swing eighth notes, as there are not many direction changes to help the line swing. Listen closely to the soloist's eighth note feel and articulation, then try to recreate that feel with a metronome, being very precise with your articulation.
3. Some of the lines in this etude (ms 39–40, 46–48, 53–55) are influenced by Hank Mobley, who had a beautiful, melodic style with lots of hip ideas, including using a tritone substitute (ms 43–44) based on a Mixolydian scale rather than a Mixolydian ♯11 scale.
4. In ms 47 and 48, an idea is stated, then played down a half step, but the chord progression is E♭7♯11 to E♭m7-A♭7. The concept is to ignore the E♭ minor II chord, thinking of the entire measure as A♭7 altered. The scale B♭ melodic minor is used on E♭7♯11, then A melodic minor on A♭7 altered. Two melodic minor scales, a half step apart.

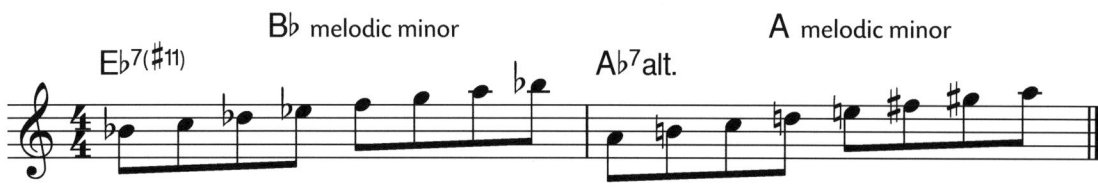

5. The line in ms 52 is based on the A♭ dominant bebop scale, adding a half step between 1 and flat 7. As was the case with the major bebop scale in *Amazing Bud*, adding a half step places chord tones on downbeats (in this case 1, 3, 5, ♭7) helping the line to sound the changes.

The A♭ dominant bebop scale works on A♭7, but notice that in ms 52 it also works on E♭m7. Since both chords are related to D♭ major and their respective scales (Dorian or Mixolydian) share the same notes, the same ideas work for both A♭7 and E♭m7.

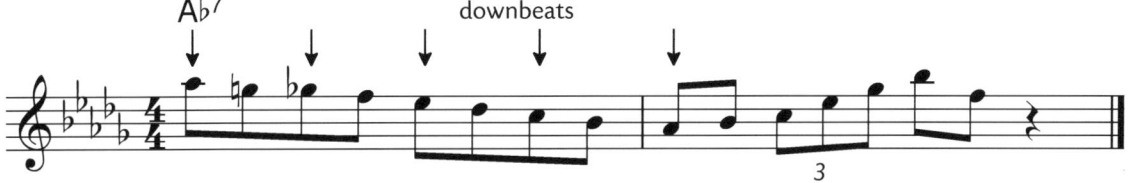

6. One way of creating a smooth transition from one chord to another is finding a common note as a "link". A common note shared between Em7-A7 in ms 51 and E♭m7-A♭7 in ms 52 is F♯ (G♭). The goal note of the line beginning in ms 51 is ultimately the F♯ on beat 1 of ms 52, the ninth of Em7. That same note becomes the third of E♭m, and the taking-off point for the line to follow.

5. Die Linie in T. 52 fußt auf der A♭-Dominant-Bebopskala, die einen zusätzlichen Halbtonschritt zwischen dem Grundton und der kleinen Septe enthält. Wie bei der Bebop-Durtonleiter in *Amazing Bud*, betont das Einfügen eines Halbtonschritts die Akkordtöne auf den Hauptschlägen (in diesem Fall Grundton, Terz, Quinte, kleine Sept).

Die A♭-Dominant-Bebopskala funktioniert auf A♭7, wie Sie aber in T. 52 sehen, auch auf E♭m7. Da beide Akkorde mit D♭-Dur verwandt sind und folglich ihre jeweiligen Skalen (dorisch bzw. mixolydisch) über denselben Tonvorrat verfügen, funktionieren die gleichen Ideen sowohl auf A♭7 als auch auf E♭m7.

6. Eine Methode, um einen glatten Übergang von einem zum nächsten Akkord zu schaffen, ist eine gemeinsame Note als Verbindung zu finden. Eine gemeinsam vorkommende Note bei Em7-A7 in T. 51 und E♭m7-A♭7 in T. 52 ist F♯ (G♭). Die Zielnote der Phrase, die in T. 51 beginnt, ist F♯ auf Schlag 1 von T. 52; F♯ ist die None von Em7 und gleichzeitig die Terz (G♭) von E♭m. Sie bildet darüber hinaus auch den Ausgangspunkt für die nächste Phrase.

Portrait of Charlie Parker, Tommy Potter, Miles Davis, Duke Jordan, and Max Roach, Three Deuces, New York, N.Y., ca. Aug. 1947

5. Miles '63

Jim Snidero

TRACK 7/19

♩ = 132 in "2"

© 2021 advance music GmbH, Mainz

*) EN = enclosed note / umspielter Ton   GT = guide tone   PT = passing tone / Durchgangston   LT = leading tone / Leitton / Annäherung

Miles '63

Miles Davis was one of the most important musicians, jazz or otherwise, of the 20th century. At the forefront of bebop in Charlie Parker's quintet in the mid-1940's, Miles went on to make enormous contributions as a leader, a true innovator that transformed jazz like no other artist. Miles' playing evolved over much of his career as well – bebop, cool jazz, modal jazz, free jazz – but was always super-relaxed, hip and tasteful.

Miles '63 is inspired by the performance of the standard *All Of You* on *Live in Europe*, recorded in Antibes, France, in 1963. One of my all-time favorites, the quintet with George Coleman, Herbie Hancock, Ron Carter and Tony Williams, created a looser, impressionistic version of hard bop, foreshadowing things to come with chromaticism and Wayne Shorter.

1. *All Of You*, or *Miles '63*, respectively, has a form of AA', but there is only one chorus in this etude, which is then followed by an open turnaround vamp (III-VI-II-V). This concept is taken from the recording mentioned above: Each soloist in Miles' group would cue the vamp, then signal the end with the melody stated in ms 85–86, followed by a 2-measure break with either the next solo or the end of the tune. Alternate notes have been provided during the double-time passages.
2. Both A sections represent a typical Miles approach during this period, using plenty of space, holding colorful notes, alluding to the melody here and there (ms 8–16, 27–28), then breaking off with turns (ms 15, 31–32).
   In ms 17–18, a simple line sets up the sustained major seventh of G♭dim, one of the most beautiful notes on a diminished chord, which uses a whole-half diminished scale.

Miles used a lot of triplets at medium tempos (ms 25–26), which help the line to rhythmically float. Here's a triplet exercise that can easily be practiced in other keys. In this case, the scale is conceived as A♭ Dorian. A♭ Dorian is the second mode of G♭ major, and since this line is diatonic, it can be used on any mode of G♭ major.

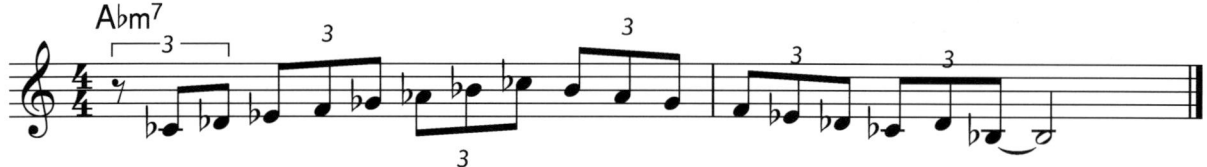

3. Miles' quintet made great use of chord extensions, especially emphasizing 11 or ♯11 (ms 31–32, 41, 46, 48, 59) and 13 (ms 15–16, 34, 39), or implying bi-tonality (ms 58 and 59). Both of these techniques add color and intrigue, helping melodies to harmonically float.
4. Though bebop musicians used (mostly diatonic) patterns, hard bop musicians expanded their use, mining sources such as Nicolas Slonimsky's *Thesaurus Of Scales And Melodic Patterns* (1947). One favorite were patterns based on a diminished scale, which were often played over a V7 chord. In ms 35–36, a triplet pattern emphasizes the most colorful notes of an A half-whole diminished.

A pianist might hear the soloist playing this pattern and adjust the chord voicing to match the the diminished sound on a V7 chord; ♭9 or ♯9, ♯11, 13.

3. Miles' Quintett spielte ausgiebig mit Akkorderweiterungen, insbesondere der 11 oder ♯11 (T. 31–32, 41, 46, 48, 59) und 13 (T. 15–16, 34, 39) und angedeuteter Bitonalität (T. 58 und 59). Diese Techniken bringen Farbe und Faszination, dabei scheinen die Melodien regelrecht über der Harmonie zu schweben.
4. Bebop-Musiker spielten (überwiegend diatonische) Patterns und Hardbop-Musiker bauten diese Technik aus, in dem sie Quellen wie *Thesaurus Of Scales And Melodic Patterns* (1947) von Nicolas Slonimsky durchforsteten. Besonders beliebt waren Patterns auf verminderten Skalen, häufig gespielt über einen V7-Akkord. In dem Triolen-Pattern in T. 35–36 werden die „farbigsten" Noten einer Halbton-Ganzton-Leiter auf A betont.

Ein Pianist könnte z. B. auf dieses vom Solisten gespielte Pattern reagieren, indem er sein V7-Akkordvoicing ändert, um es dem verminderten Sound mit den Optionstönen ♭9 oder ♯9, ♯11 und 13 anzupassen.

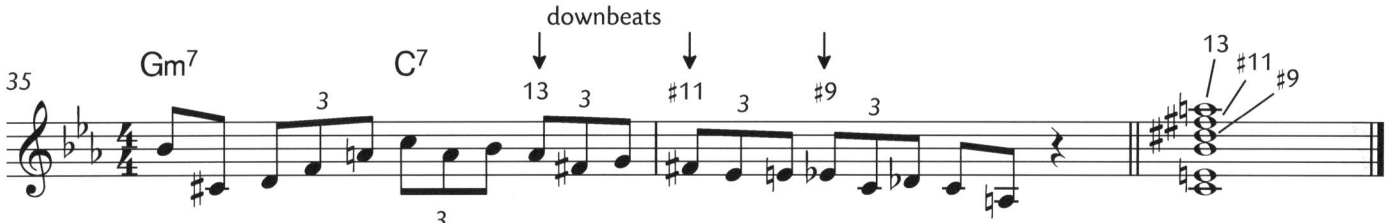

5. The vamp beginning at ms 41 is based on a 4-measure turnaround chord progression, III-VI-II-V. This is a very common way of extending a tune, especially after the out (final) head is played. As mentioned above, Miles also used this as a vamp between solos, with this version being inspired by the concepts of George and Herbie.

This section is a good example of how the "arc" of a solo could evolve, sort of a macro view: It begins with plenty of space using colorful fragments (e. g. extensions) that develop melodically for eight measures. Then more tension is introduced using V7 alterations (ms 50, 52, 54) and chord substitutions (ms 57, 60, 64). This is followed by eight measures of double time, highlighting virtuosity and increasing intensity, finishing out with the blues, bringing a refined earthiness to the last section while still maintaining intensity until the melodic cue to end.

5. Der Vamp ab T. 41 basiert auf dem viertaktigen Turnaround III-VI-II-V. Dies ist eine einfache Methode, um ein Stück zu verlängern, insbesondere nach dem finalen Erscheinen des Themas. Wie oben erwähnt, verwendete Miles diese Akkordfolge als Vamp zwischen den Soli; die Version in der Etüde ist von Konzepten von George und Herbie beeinflusst.

Dieser Abschnitt zeigt eindrucksvoll wie sich der „Bogen" eines Solos entwickeln könnte, quasi durch die Makrolinse betrachtet: Der Anfang beginnt großräumig mit farbigen Fragmenten (z. B. Erweiterungen), die sich organisch über acht Takte weiterentwickeln. Danach wird größere Spannung durch alterierte Dominantseptakkorde/V7-Alterationen (T. 50, 52, 54) und Akkordsubstitutionen (T. 57, 60, 64) erzeugt. Dann werden acht Takte Double-Time mit größter Virtuosität und wachsender Intensität gespielt. Im Schlussteil kommt der raffinierte aber erdige Blues-Sound: Hier wird die Intensität bis zum Hinweis auf den Schluss aufrechterhalten.

Solo Arc

Solo-Bogen

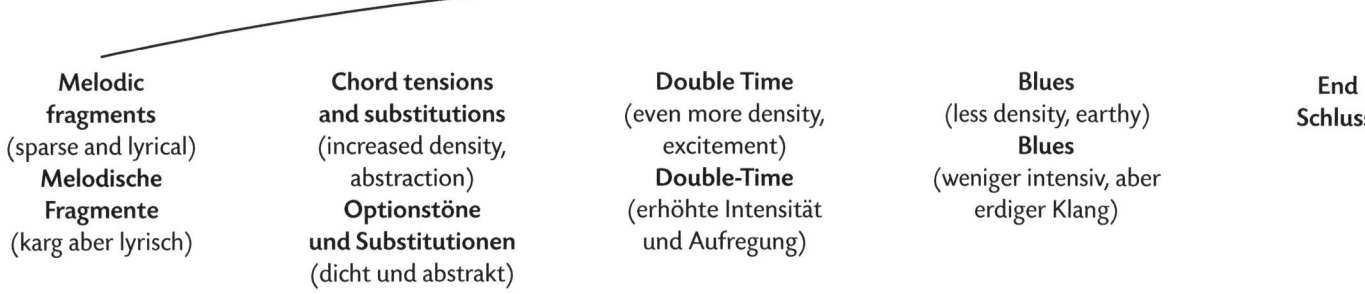

This is actually one good example of overall pacing and development of any solo, as well as how individual ideas are timed relative to one another. For example, the placement of the chord substitution F♯m^7-B^7 or the color change from Fm^7 to F$^{7\sharp11}$ (ms 57).

6. A micro view of this section would be an examination of individual ideas. Some of them sound the changes, some sustain extensions, and some are a blues idea over an entire turnaround. An attractive aspect of these ideas is that a) there's a wide variety of color, and b) they stand on their own, making them very useable building blocks of vocabulary.

7. The line in ms 69 demonstrates a way of adding another chromatic note to a dominant bebop scale while keeping fundamental chord tones on downbeats. When descending from the ninth of a dominant chord (in this case C on B♭^{7}) beginning on a downbeat, add a half step, then continue down on the dominant bebop scale.
Here's the same idea in eighth notes, starting on beat 1 and finishing out differently to fit a 4-measure II-V-I.

Dieses Solo verdeutlicht das Pacing (Einteilung der allgemeinen Geschwindigkeit und Aufbau) und die Entwicklung eines Solos: Darüber hinaus sieht man, wie einzelne Ideen zeitlich aufgereiht werden, z. B. die Platzierung der Akkord-Substitution F♯m-B^7 oder der Klangfarbenwechsel von Fm^7 zu F$^{7\sharp11}$ (T. 57).

6. Eine Nahansicht/Mikro-Betrachtung dieses Abschnitts lässt die einzelnen Ideen aufleuchten. Mal werden die Akkorde ausgespielt, mal werden Erweiterungen gehalten und zeitweilig werden Blues-Ideen über einem kompletten Turnaround eingesetzt. Das Schöne an diesen Ideen ist ihr Facettenreichtum und dass sie für sich stehen können: Man kann sie als Einzelelemente gut in anderen Solos einbauen.

7. Die Linie in T. 69 verdeutlicht, wie man einen weiteren chromatischen Ton in eine Dominant-Bebopskala einfügt, wobei die Hauptnoten des Akkords auf den starken Schlägen bleiben. Von der None eines Dominantakkords (hier C auf B♭^{7}) absteigend, fügt man einen Halbton ein und spielt ab dem Grundton die bereits bekannte Dominant-Bebopskala.
Hier die gleiche Idee in Achtelnoten: Die Linie beginnt auf dem ersten Schlag und wird am Ende im Sinne der II-V-I-Verbindung mit ganztaktigen Wechseln abgewandelt.

As mentioned on *Pure Silver*, ideas that work on V7 also work on the related IIm^7 (B♭^{7} and Fm^7 are chords/modes of E♭ major). So this scale could be used, for example, on a F minor vamp. In fact, that's exactly what's happening on *The Messengers* in ms 68! Here's that idea in eighth notes adjusted to fit a 4-measure II-V-I.

Wie bereits bei *Pure Silver* erwähnt, funktionieren V7-Ideen ebenfalls auf den zugehörigen IIm^7-Akkorden (denn sowohl B♭^{7} als auch Fm^7 sind leitereigene Akkorde bzw. Modi von E♭-Dur). Es wäre also möglich, diese Skala bei einem Fm-Vamp einzusetzen – genau wie in T. 68 von *The Messengers*! Hier die gleiche Idee in Achtelnoten, wiederum angepasst an eine II-V-I mit ganztaktigen Akkordwechseln.

Understanding how chords and scales are interrelated gives vocabulary much more flexibility, allowing you to apply an idea over more than one chord.

Ein Verständnis für den Zusammenhang von Akkorden und Tonleitern bringt eine größere Flexibilität beim Spielen mit sich, weil Sie eine einzige Idee dann auf verschiedene Akkorde anwenden können.

Bird And Diz*

The collaboration between Charlie "Bird" Parker and Dizzy Gillespie between about 1945 and 1955 was probably the most important of the bebop era. Though Bird's improvising was more influential on the world of music (we'll talk more about Bird on the last etude), Dizzy actually equaled Bird in his inventiveness and virtuosity. Dizzy also had a very deep understanding of harmony, mentoring and influencing many of the greatest bebop musicians.

Bird And Diz is inspired by Tadd Dameron's *Hot House*, considered a kind of "anthem" of the bebop movement. Bird and Dizzy recorded it many times, and in fact, it was the one tune they selected to perform on the only existing nationwide TV show (1952) of these two giants. *Hot House* in turn is based on the chord progression to the standard *What Is This Thing Called Love* and contains some lines that were fairly abstract at the time, reminiscent of harmonic concepts associated with Dizzy. So this etude is as much about Dizzy's harmony as Bird's and Dizzy's improvising.

1. The form of *Bird And Diz* is AA'BA, with the second chorus cut short with a tag repeating the last phrase over an G^7 pedal. The chord progression on the A section is quite smooth, as Fm^6 in the third measure is related to $Dm^{7\flat5}$.

The minor II-V of $Dm^{7\flat5}$-G^7 normally goes to C minor, so there's a nice surprise when C major arrives at the end of the A sections. This also occurs on the last four measures of the standard *Stella By Starlight*.

2. As mentioned in *Amazing Bud*, syncopation is a hallmark of bebop. There are many examples of syncopated rhythms and lines throughout *Bird And Diz*, but the trick is to find the right combination of syncopated and non-syncopated phrases that create balance and importantly, flow.
There are several examples of this balance in *Bird And Diz*. A good one is ms 1–4, which have relatively few syncopations, with interest generated by the harmony implied in the line. Ms 5–8 are highly syncopated, with the earthiness of the blues emphasized in the line.

---

* To avoid an awkward page turn, the music starts on page 38.

3. As is the case with *Hot House*, it's unusual to state a completely new theme on the second A (ms 9–16), and this is where the line becomes more abstract. However, on both the first and second As, a 2-measure line is played over the minor II-V. The second measure of this line is then repeated down a whole step, this time over a minor chord, creating an attractive dissonance similar to Dizzy with a leading tone on a downbeat and minor major 7.

4. On the C^7 chord in ms 2, 10 and 26, two different alterations are used. The first implies the tritone substitute of Gb^7, but the second implies $C^{9\sharp 11\ 13}$, an unexpected color change not normally used on a V7 chord going to a I minor chord, and reminiscent of *Hot House*. Try practicing these alterations around the circle of fourths.

5. As mentioned above, Fm^6 is related to Dm^{7b5}, so basically anything that's played on Fm^6 works on Dm^{7b5}, including F blues ideas (ms 5, 29, 61). As was the case with *Miles '63*, the blues adds earthiness to a fairly abstract bebop piece.

   In fact, the blues is such a strong sound that both Bird and Dizzy would use it on virtually any chord. Here we have an C blues over C^{maj7} (ms 7–8, 31–32), Dm^{7b5} (13), and G^7 (tag).

6. On the last four measures of the bridge (ms 21–24, 53–56), the normal chords are two measures of Ab^7, to either a measure each of Dm^7 and G^7, or two measures of G^7. However, on the head in ms 21–24, the line, based on a half-whole diminished scale, outlines both an Ab^7 and an G^7 chord with a 13, $\sharp$11 and $\sharp$9, creating an edgy dissonance similar to *Hot House*. This would be a challenging idea to practice around the circle of fourths in twelve keys.

Die T. 5–8 enthalten wiederum viele Synkopen, wobei das Erdige des Blues in der Linie betont wird.

3. Es ist ungewöhnlich, dass ein Stück (wie z. B. *Hot House*) im zweiten A-Teil ein völlig neues Thema einführt (T. 9–16): Dadurch wirkt die Linie etwas abstrakter. Dennoch wird in beiden A-Teilen eine zweitaktige Linie über die II-V-Verbindung in Moll gespielt. Der zweite Takt dieser Linie wird dann einen Ganzton tiefer wiederholt – hier über einem Mollakkord (mit großer Septime) –, und erzeugt eine attraktive Dissonanz nach Art von Dizzy, mit Leitton auf dem Schlag.

4. Zwei verschiedene alterierte Töne werden beim C^7-Akkord in T. 2, 10 und 26 eingesetzt: Der erste impliziert die Tritonussubstitution Gb^7, während der zweite $C^{9\sharp 11\ 13}$ andeutet – ein unerwarteter Klangfarbenwechsel, der normalerweise nicht bei einer Progression vom V7-Akkord auf einen I-Mollakkord eingesetzt wird – eine Erinnerung an *Hot House*. Versuchen Sie, diese Alterationen im Quartenzirkel zu üben.

5. Wie oben erwähnt, ist Fm^6 mit Dm^{7b5} verwandt, aus diesem Grund funktioniert alles, was auf Fm^6 gespielt wird, auch auf Dm^{7b5}, unter anderem F-Blues-Ideen (T. 5, 29, 61). Ähnlich wie bei *Miles '63*, verleiht der Blues einem relativ abstrakten Bebop-Stück eine gewisse Erdigkeit.

   Im übrigen ist der Blues ein so prägnanter Sound, dass Bird und auch Dizzy ihn auf fast jedem Akkord anwendet haben. Hier haben wir einen C-Blues auf C^{maj7} (T. 7–8, 31–32), Dm^{7b5} (13) und G^7 (Coda).

6. In den letzten vier Takten der Überleitung (T. 21–24, 53–56) wäre die übliche Harmonie zwei Takte Ab^7, gefolgt von entweder einem Takt Dm^7 und einem Takt G^7 oder zwei Takten G^7. Allerdings beinhaltet die Linie des Themenkopfs in T. 21–24 (die auf der Halbton-Ganzton-Leiter basiert) sowohl einen Ab^7- als auch einen G^7-Akkord mit den Alterationen 13, $\sharp$11 und $\sharp$9. Diese kreieren eine scharfe Dissonanz ähnlich wie in *Hot House*. Es wäre eine große Herausforderung, diese anspruchsvolle Idee in allen Tonarten durch den Quartenzirkel zu üben.

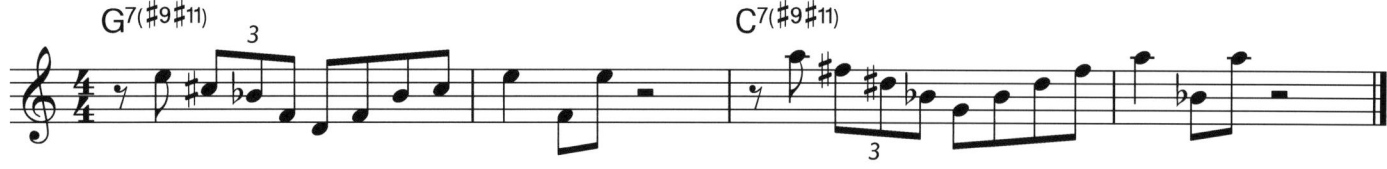

7. Ms 35 demonstrates a common technique Bird would use over a minor chord, playing two beats of Fm, then two beats on C$^{7\flat9}$ (I-V-I over a static minor chord). All of these notes are also in the F harmonic minor scale. This would be a good one to practice in every key.

7. In T. 35 wird eine Technik gezeigt, die häufig von Bird auf Mollakkorden angewendet wurde, wonach er zwei Schläge auf Fm gefolgt von zwei Schlägen auf C$^{7\flat9}$ spielte (I-V-I über einem statischen Mollakkord). Alle diese Töne kommen auch in F harmonisch Moll vor. Dieses Konzept könnte man auch wunderbar in jeder Tonart üben.

8. One favorite concept of Bird's was to use a major II-V sound in the first part of a minor II-V, creating a surprising brightness (ms 34, 37–38, 41).
9. Bird and Dizzy would sometimes balance playing the changes with diatonic lines or even song quotes (see *Bird* etude), especially on the bridge to *Hot House* (ms 49–52).

8. Ein Lieblingskonzept von Bird war die Verwendung eines II-V-Klangs in Dur im ersten Teil einer II-V in Moll, was eine erstaunliche Brillanz erzeugt (T. 34, 37–38, 41).
9. Gelegentlich haben Bird und Dizzy das Ausspielen der Akkorde durch diatonische Linien oder Songzitate ausgeglichen (siehe *Bird*-Etüde), zum Beispiel in der Bridge von *Hot House* (T. 49–52).

Portrait of Dizzy Gillespie, New York, N.Y., ca. May 1947

Portrait of Fats Navarro, Charlie Rouse, Ernie Henry, and Tadd Dameron, New York, N.Y., between 1946 and 1948

▶ TRACK 8/20

6. Bird And Diz

♩ = 144

Chorus 1

Jim Snidero

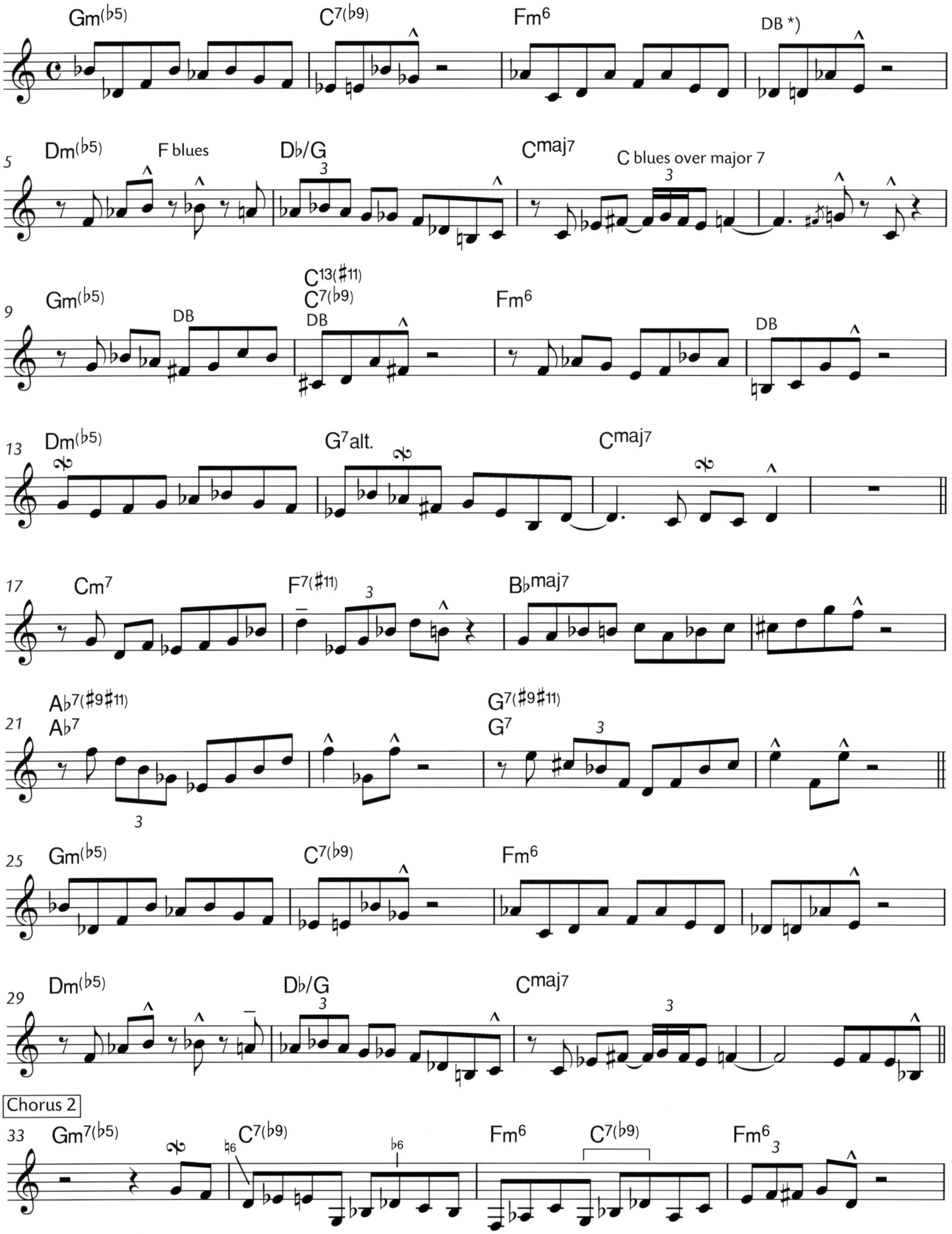

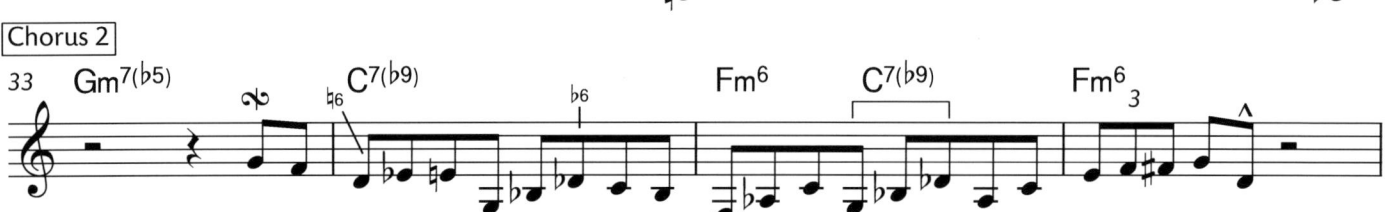

*) DB = downbeat leading tone / Leitton auf (betonter) Zählzeit EN = enclosed note / umspielter Ton GT = guide tone
PT = passing tone / Durchgangston LT = leading tone / Leitton / Annäherung

7. Straight Trane

Jim Snidero

*) EN = enclosed note / umspielter Ton GT = guide tone PT = passing tone / Durchgangston LT = leading tone / Leitton / Annäherung

Straight Trane

Like Miles Davis, John Coltrane is one of the rare artists that had a profound impact on jazz and beyond. "Trane" took hard bop to its ultimate technical heights with records like *Giant Steps* before revolutionizing improvisation with chord substitutions, pentatonics, and free music, culminating in his masterpiece *A Love Supreme*. Trane was also an inspirational figure. An extremely hard worker, he developed from an above-average hard bop musician to a towering master saxophonist and artist.

Contrasting to the solo arc discussed in *Miles '63*, Trane would often start strong and dense, and sustain that concept throughout an entire solo, which is the case on *Straight Trane*. It's fairly intense throughout, basically a straight line of intensity, with no substantial peaks or valleys within the overall pacing of the piece.

Straight Trane is based on Trane's *Straight Street,* a quasi-jazz standard from his debut 1957 recording as a leader, *Coltrane*. The form is AABA, but it is unusual in that each section is 12 measures long. The key of concert E♭ minor has technical challenges, as well as the bridge, which begins in concert B and then 4 measures of concert D.

1. With eight keys represented, *Straight Trane* is the most comprehensive study in II-V in this book.
    a. 1-measure II-Vs; Bm⁷-E⁷, Am⁷-D⁷, Gm⁷-C⁷, Fm⁷-B♭⁷, Fm⁷♭⁵-B♭⁷, F♯m⁷-B⁷
    b. 2-measure II-Vs; Fm⁷♭⁵-B♭⁷, Em⁷-A⁷, E♭m⁷-A♭⁷, D♭m⁷-G♭⁷
2. Each A section begins with four 1-measure II-Vs, with the last finally resolving into the key of the tune, E♭ minor. These II-Vs move sequentially down in whole steps, with each II-V resolving to the next II-V. So, I becomes II in the next measure.
   Hard-bop musicians tended to use mostly diatonic ideas on a series of 1-measure II-Vs. This is because there's enough tension and release happening with the harmony that lines don't necessarily need tension on V chords (e. g. altered, diminished) to create interest. Here's a diatonic exercise using guide tones to sound the changes on descending 1-measure II-Vs. Practice in the other six keys as well.

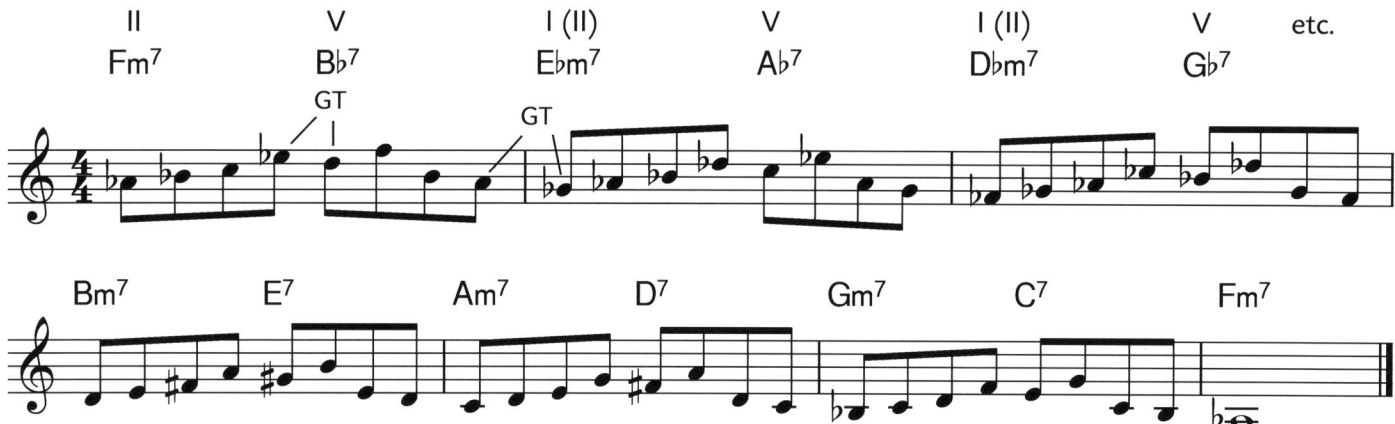

3. As mentioned in *Monktified*, it's very common and natural to group ideas in 2-measure phrases. In this piece, ideas are framed by rests (ms 26–29, 62–65), linked by a II-V-I resolution (ms 30–33, 46–49, 50–53, 70–73, 78–81) or use a pickup to a 2-measure idea (ms 9–13, 57–61). This variety of approaches to 2-measure phrasing provides interest in timing, but at their core, they are 2-measure ideas. Try memorizing some of them.
4. There are three sounds used on minor II-Vs;
   a. Harmonic minor (ms 7, 23, 47)
   b. Altered (ms 11, 43, 55)
   c. Dominant 7 bebop (ms 70).
   Harmonic minor ideas tend to be smoother, while altered ideas generally increase tension. Dominant 7 bebop adds a surprising brightness over a minor II-V.
5. One common technique on chord progressions moving quickly in half steps is to repeat the same idea in each key (ms 36–37). This can sound very solid and logical, and in this case, contrasts with other lines that weave through changes.
6. As mentioned in *Bird And Diz*, when chords are related via modes, basically any idea that works over one chord will work on the other related chords. In ms 57–59, an idea that could easily be used on A♭m⁷-D♭⁷-G♭maj, including the D♭⁷ dominant bebop scale, works on Fm⁷♭⁵-B♭⁷-E♭m. This is because A♭ Dorian and F Locrian are modes of G♭ major.

3. Wie in *Monktified* erwähnt, werden Ideen häufig in 2-taktigen Phrasen gruppiert. In diesem Stück werden die Ideen von Pausen eingerahmt (T. 26–29, 62–65), durch eine Auflösung verbunden (T. 30–33, 46–49, 50–53, 70–73, 78–81) oder es gibt einen Auftakt zu einer 2-taktigen Idee (T. 9–13, 57–61). Diese verschiedenen Methoden der 2-taktigen Phrasierung erzeugen zwar ein abwechslungsreiches Timing, bleiben aber im Kern 2-taktige Ideen. Versuchen Sie, einige dieser Licks auswendig zu lernen.
4. Man verwendet drei Skalen auf II-V-Verbindungen in Moll;
   a. harmonisch Moll (T. 7, 23, 47)
   b. alteriert (T. 11, 43, 55)
   c. Bebop-Dominant-Sept (T. 70).
   Harmonische Ideen in Moll klingen etwas geschmeidiger, während alterierte Ideen generell die Spannung erhöhen. Die Dominant-Bebopskala bringt über eine II-V in Moll gespielt einen überraschend hellen Klang.
5. Eine häufig benutzte Technik auf schnelle Akkordfolgen in Halbtonschritten ist die Wiederholung derselben Idee in jeder Tonart (T. 36–37). Dadurch klingt die Musik etwas solider und logischer und erzeugt, wie hier gezeigt, einen Kontrast zu anderen Linien, die die Akkorde ausspielen.
6. Wie in *Bird And Diz* erwähnt, funktioniert im Grunde jede Idee über einen bestimmten Akkord auch über andere Akkorde, solange diese über Modi verwandt sind. In T. 57–59 wird eine Idee, die gut zu A♭m⁷-D♭⁷-G♭maj passen würde (einschließlich der D♭⁷-Dominant-Bebopskala), über Fm⁷♭⁵-B♭⁷-E♭m gespielt: Dies ist möglich, weil sowohl A♭ dorisch als auch F lokrisch Modi von G♭-Dur sind.

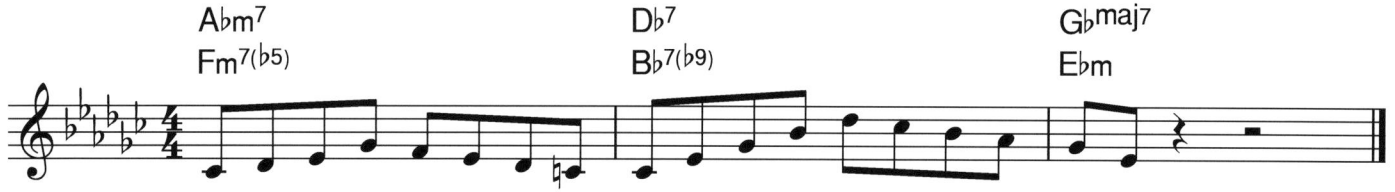

8. Freddie

TRACK 10/22 (slow), 11/23 (fast)

Jim Snidero

Slower: ♩ = 88
Faster: ♩ = 120

© 2021 advance music GmbH, Mainz

*) EN = enclosed note / umspielter Ton   GT = guide tone   PT = passing tone / Durchgangston   LT = leading tone / Leitton / Annäherung

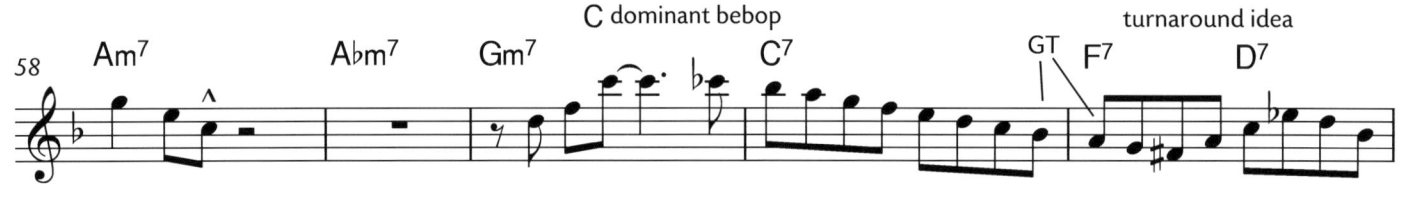

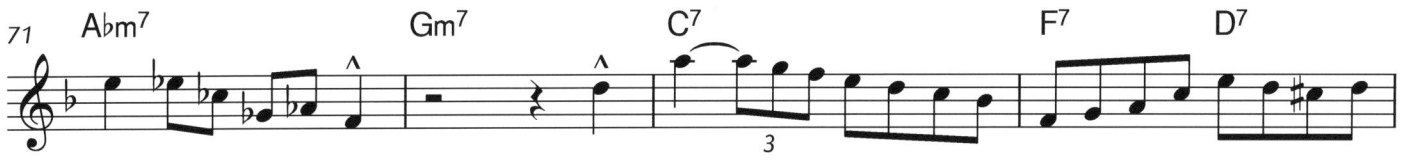

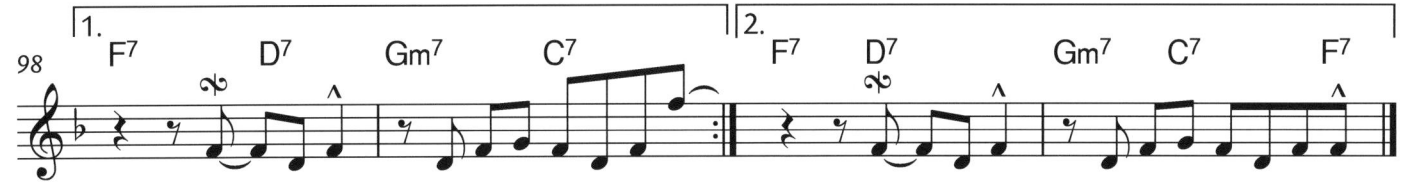

Freddie

Freddie Hubbard developed one of the most important trumpet styles in jazz history. His sound has influenced countless trumpet players and his technique was rarely matched on the trumpet. Freddie played with *The Jazz Messengers* from 1961 to 1966, and was a sideman on many important recordings throughout the 1960s, including albums by Herbie Hancock, Dexter Gordon and John Coltrane, among others. His leader dates evolved from hardbop on Blue Note to influential post-bop recordings on CTI, with several originals becoming jazz standards.

The two most common keys for the blues are concert B♭ (*Monktified*) and concert F, which is the key of *Freddie* and Freddie Hubbard's blues *Birdlike* (1961). Freddie's style during this period was fairly calculated, flawlessly executing prepared material with a tremendous amount of flair.

1. There is a slower and faster version of *Freddie* on the play-along, with articulation from the faster one included here. Generally, trumpet and other wind instrument players articulate less on faster tempos than on slower ones. Play the slower version first to master the etude, then go on to the faster version. At faster tempos, don't try to feel every beat, which can make the time sound stiff. Rather, try to feel the music 'in 2', meaning beats 1 and 3, or even full measures, especially at very fast tempos.
2. Technique obviously becomes an issue when trying to execute lines cleanly at faster tempos, so one common solution is to use longer segments of scales, which tend to be easier than shifting melodic fragments (ms 28, 31–32, 44–45, 48, 61). At slower tempos, longer scale passages might sound boring, but they can work well at faster tempos.
3. Freddie often took his time on faster tempos, using longer rests to let the music breath and frame ideas, as mentioned in *Miles '63*. Faster tempos are more challenging for the rhythm section as well, so longer rests give them a chance to gel and keep the music relaxed. Try setting a metronome to about half note = 120, and practice a 4-measure cycle of playing about 2 measures, then resting about 2 measures.
4. On the head, ms 4 uses the tritone substitute F♯m^7-B^7 resolving to B♭^{7}. Similar to the concept on *Pure Silver* in ms 44, this idea is based on the F♯ Dorian or B Mixolydian scale (no ♯11), creating a hip dissonance (E on a F^7) before resolving to B♭^{7}. Here's an idea that clearly outlines a tritone sub II-V, which could be practiced around the circle of fourths.

5. On both the head and several solo choruses, "Bird Changes" are used in ms 7–8, moving chromatically from III (Am⁷) to ♭III (A♭m⁷) to II (Gm⁷) in measure 9. This provides a nice color change outside the key of the tune, and can be used on any blues when soloing.

6. Freddie used a lot of lines built on bebop scales during this period, especially the dominant bebop (ms 32, 42, 45, 60–61, 68–69). On *Miles '63,* we saw that, beginning on a downbeat, you can add a half step between 2 and 1 on a descending dominant bebop scale. On *Freddie* in measures 31–32 and 44–45, beginning on a downbeat, a half step is added between 6 and 5 on a descending dominant bebop scale. Here's an idea using this concept on a II-V-I in E♭ major. Try practicing it in every key:

5. Im Thema und in einigen Solo-Chorusen werden in T. 7–8 „Bird Changes" eingesetzt, die in T. 9 von III (Am⁷) über ♭III (A♭m⁷) zu II (Gm⁷) chromatisch absteigen. Dadurch wird ein bunter Farbenwechsel außerhalb der Tonart der Melodie erzeugt. Diese Besonderheit kann man bei allen Blues-Soli anwenden.

6. Freddie arbeitete in dieser Zeit häufig mit Bebop-Skalen, besonders der Dominant-Bebopskala (T. 32, 42, 45, 60–61, 68–69). In *Miles '63* haben wir gesehen, dass man in der absteigenden Bebop-Dominant-Skala, wenn man auf dem Schlag beginnt, einen Halbtonschritt zwischen der None und dem Grundton der Tonleiter einfügen kann. In T. 31–32 und 44–45 von *Freddie* beginnt man wiederum auf dem Schlag mit der absteigenden Dominant-Bebopskala und fügt einen Halbtonschritt zwischen der Sexte und der Quinte ein. Das nächste Beispiel zeigt das Konzept über eine II-V-I in E♭-Dur. Probieren Sie, dieses Konzept in allen Tonarten zu spielen.

7. A 2-measure turnaround is used often on the last two measures of the blues, but it can sound a bit mechanical if you play it on every chorus. On the first three solo choruses of *Freddie*, the turnaround isn't played, with the line before resolving, followed by a long rest, which is a natural place to pause on a blues form. Finally, in ms 62–63 and ms 86–87, the turnaround is played, propelling the solo to the next section. It's all about pacing and picking the most musical spots to play the turnaround.

8. To contrast chromatic or chord substitution ideas, Freddie sometimes used song-like diatonic melodies, similar to a bugle call, to bring an earthy playfulness to his solos (ms 24–26, 52–55, 66).

7. In den letzten zwei Takten des Blues wird oft ein 2-taktiger Turnaround verwendet, aber dies klingt bei übermäßigem Einsatz in jedem Chorus etwas mechanisch. In den ersten drei Chorusen in *Freddie* wird der Turnaround nicht gespielt: Die vorherige Linie wird aufgelöst und es folgt eine längere Pause, wobei eben diese beiden letzten Takte im Blues eine sehr natürliche Stelle zum Pausieren sind. Der Turnaround taucht erst in T. 62–63 und T. 86–87 auf und bringt dem Solo am Übergang in den nächsten Abschnitt viel Schwung. Es ist also wichtig, an das Pacing zu denken und den Turnaround sinnvoll im musikalischen Kontext zu platzieren.

8. Freddie setzte gelegentlich gesangliche diatonische Melodien (wie Fanfaren) als Kontrast zu chromatische Ideen oder Akkord-Substitutionen ein, um eine bodenständige Verspieltheit in seine Solos zu bringen (T. 24–26, 52–55, 66).

9. One For Sonny

Jim Snidero

© 2021 advance music GmbH, Mainz

*) EN = enclosed note / umspielter Ton GT = guide tone PT = passing tone / Durchgangston LT = leading tone / Leitton / Annäherung

One For Sonny

The two most important tenor saxophonists in jazz history are arguably John Coltrane and Sonny Rollins, one way or another influencing virtually every tenor player from the hard-bop era onward. Rollins was a hugely inventive improvisor, and as the great drummer Jimmy Cobb told me, "the man" around 1957, the year that he recorded the jazz standard ballad *I Can't Get Started* on *One Night At The Village Vanguard*, the inspiration for *One For Sonny*. (For direct comparison, Coltrane's *Straight Street* was recorded within months of *I Can't Get Started*.)

Many jazz musicians consider the mid/late 1950s to be Rollins' definitive period, one that produced several monumental recordings including *Saxophone Colossus*, *Tenor Madness* and the above-mentioned Vanguard record. Rollins' greatest influence as an improvisor was Charlie Parker, abstracting Bird's concepts into a sort of collage, combined with incredible tone and musicality.

I Can't Get Started has the standard AABA form, but presents a harmonic challenge in ms 3–4 of the A section, with II-V descending in half steps.

1. Ballads are one of the most difficult tempos to perform. For sure, musicality is essential, with vocabulary taking somewhat of a secondary role. Of course, the best way to learn how to be musical is to listen to musical artists. Musicality definitely has an 'X factor', tapping into, for lack of a better word, the spirit of the artist, bringing a timeless quality to the music that can be very moving. Here are three common qualities present in a musical ballad performance. Listen closely to the recording and see if you can replicate these qualities;
   a. Tone: In a technical sense, this is probably the most critical factor when playing a ballad. Rollins had a huge sound, but it also had incredible "center", holding the sound together and providing more impact and projection. And there was a lot of color and "buzz" surrounding the core of the sound, adding nuance and personality. These are timeless qualities to tone that many great players strive to achieve.
   b. Dynamic shading: Good ballad performers vary dynamics to create, among other things, intimacy, anticipation, tension and release. They could be very subtle, for example slight tapering at the end of sustained notes, or more deliberate, emphasizing a phrase such as ms 22–23. There are no rules, but there are certain common tendencies, including playing higher passages louder, lower ones, softer.
   c. Vibrato: Again, there are no rules, just observations and tendencies. Swing-era artists often used a wider/faster vibrato throughout the entire value of the note. Most bebop/hard-bop artists used a narrower vibrato and vibrated a bit slower, but it's all about personal preference. Rollins used vibrato often, Trane hardly at

One For Sonny

John Coltrane und Sonny Rollins sind vermutlich die zwei wichtigsten Tenorsaxophonisten der Jazzgeschichte und beeinflussten auf die eine oder andere Weise vermutlich fast alle Tenorspieler seit der Hardbop-Ära. Rollins war ein unglaublich erfinderischer Improvisator: Wie mir der große Drummer Jimmy Cobb erzählte, war er „der Mann" von 1957, dem Jahr seiner Aufnahme der Jazz-Ballade *I Can't Get Started* auf *One Night At The Village Vanguard*, die wiederum die Inspiration für *One For Sonny* lieferte. (Zum direkten Vergleich: Coltranes *Straight Street* wurde einige Monate später als *I Can't Get Started* aufgenommen).

Viele Jazzmusiker betrachten die mittleren bis späten 1950er-Jahre als Rollins' maßgebliche Phase, in der einige große Aufnahmen wie zum Beispiel *Saxophone Colossus*, *Tenor Madness* und die oben erwähnte *Vanguard*-Aufnahme entstanden. Charlie Parker hat als Improvisator den größten Einfluss auf Rollins genommen; Rollins abstrahierte Birds Konzepte zu einer Art Collage und intensivierte sie mit einem wunderbaren Ton und Musikalität.

I Can't Get Started verwendet die übliche AABA-Form, stellt aber in Hinblick auf die Harmonik eine Herausforderung dar: Die Takte 3 bis 4 des A-Teils bestehen aus einer in Halbtonschritten absteigenden Folge von II-V-Verbindungen.

1. Balladen sind vom Tempo her nicht leicht vorzutragen. Hier spielt Musikalität eine entscheidende Rolle, während stilistische Figuren eine sekundäre Angelegenheit sind. Musikalität kann man sich am besten durch das Anhören von Künstlern mit hoher Musikalität aneignen. Musikalität besteht ohne Zweifel aus einer Art „X-Faktor", der dem Geist des Musikers innewohnt und eine zeitlose und bewegende Eigenschaft in die Musik bringt.
   Die Aufnahme zeigt drei allgemeine Merkmale, die in einer musikalischen Darbietung einer Ballade präsent sein sollten. Hören Sie sehr genau zu und versuchen Sie, diese Eigenschaften in Ihrem Spiel zu replizieren:
   a. Ton/Sound: Technisch gesehen ist der Ton wohl der wesentlichste Faktor beim Spielen einer Ballade. Rollins besaß zwar einen großen Sound, aber dieser war gleichzeitig unglaublich zentriert, indem er den Klang bündelte und somit eine größere Wirkung und Projektion erzielte. Der Klangkern hatte sehr viel Farbe und „Buzz" und verlieh seinem Spiel Nuancen und Charakter. Das sind zeitlose Qualitäten, die viele große Musiker angestrebt haben.
   b. Dynamische Schattierung: Balladenexperten sind in der Lage, die Dynamik zu variieren, um Eigenschaften wie Innigkeit, Vorfreude, Spannung und Entspannung auszudrücken. Die Schattierungen sind teilweise höchst subtil, wie zum Beispiel das Ausklingen gehaltener Noten, oder aber wie in T. 22–23 ganz bewusst eingesetzt, um eine Phrase zu unterstreichen.

2. It's common to add ideas to enhance the melody on a ballad. In each 2-measure section from ms 1–6, the melody is stated in the first measure, followed by a rhythmic/phrasing variation in measure 2, scale fragments over descending II-Vs (ms 4), and an altered idea over V7 (ms 6).
3. In ms 7–8, substitutions similar to Rollins' are used on the III-VI-II-V turnaround, moving chromatically down – B♭7, A7, A♭7 – until the II chord, which has a chord quality changed from Dm7 to D7, then finally V7 altered, G7alt. You can almost always use chord substitution, even if the rhythm section is playing the normal changes. As long as they are logical, and importantly, you hear them, they will usually sound good, bringing more interest to a solo.

   c. Vibrato: Hier gibt es wiederum keine festen Regeln, sondern lediglich Beobachtungen und Tendenzen. Swing-Künstler pflegten ein weiteres/schnelleres Vibrato durch den ganzen Notenwert aufrecht zu erhalten. Die Mehrheit der Bebop-/Hardbop-Künstler hat ein etwas engeres und langsameres Vibrato eingesetzt, letztlich geht es aber dabei um persönliche Vorlieben. Rollins hat oft mit Vibrato gespielt, Trane dafür fast gar nicht. Hören Sie genau zu, wo die Musiker ihr Vibrato an- und absetzen und wie weit und wandelbar es ist.
2. Es ist üblich, die Balladenmelodie mit Ideen und Verzierungen zu bereichern. In jedem zweitaktigen Abschnitt von T. 1–6 wird die Melodie jeweils im ersten Takt vorgestellt und im nächsten Takt durch eine rhythmische/phrasierungsmäßige Variation (T. 2), Skalenausschnitte über absteigende II-V (T. 4) und eine alterierte Idee über V7 (T. 6) erweitert.
3. Substitutionen nach Art von Rollins werden beim III-VI-II-V-Turnaround in T. 7–8 eingesetzt, welcher sich chromatisch abwärts bewegt – B♭7, A7, A♭7 – bis zum II-Akkord, der hier nicht als Mollakkord Dm7, sondern als D7 erscheint. Das Ende des Turnarounds markiert der V7-Akkord G7 alt. Es ist fast überall möglich, Akkord-Substitutionen zu verwenden, auch wenn die Rhythmusgruppe die normalen Akkorde spielt. Solange sie logisch bleiben und Sie sie „hören" können (sehr wichtig), werden sie gut klingen und Ihr Solo beleben.

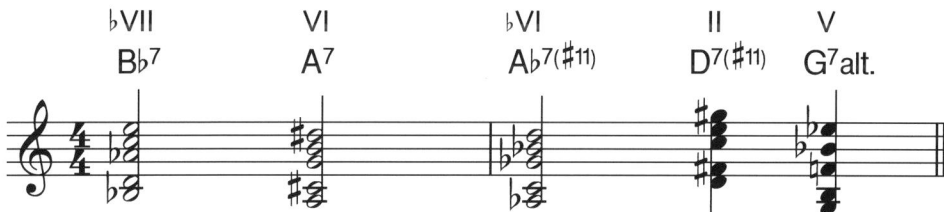

4. Unlike II-Vs descending in whole steps (*Straight Trane*), II-Vs descending chromatically (ms 3–4, 11–12, 27–28) don't resolve to the next II-V. But the last two II-Vs – Am7-D7 A♭m7-D♭7 – function as II7 (D7), then ♭II7 (D♭7), with their related IIm in front of each. D♭7 is the V7 tritone sub for G7, A♭m-D♭7 is the II-V tritone sub for Dm7-G7, resolving to I.

4. Im Gegensatz zu den in Ganzton absteigenden II-V-Verbindungen (*Straight Trane*), lösen sich chromatisch absteigende II-V (T. 3–4, 11–12, 27–28) nicht in die nächste II-V auf. Dennoch funktionieren die letzten beiden II-V-Verbindungen – Am7-D7 A♭m7-D♭7 – jeweils als II7 (D7) und ♭II7 (D♭7), mit der dazugehörigen II. D♭7 ist die Tritonussubstitution für G7 und A♭m7-D♭7 die II-V-Tritonussubstitution für Dm7-G7, die sich zu I auflöst.

5. In ms 15 on beat 3 and 4, the chord progression Fm7-Bb7 functions as IVm-bVII to I in ms 16. Sometimes called a "backdoor" II-V, this is a very common and smooth way to get back to a I chord. It's also common to eliminate IVm, simply going I-bVII-I.

5. Die Akkordfolge Fm7-Bb7 auf Schlag 3 und 4 in T. 15 ist eine IVm-bVII-Verbindung in Bezug auf I (T. 16). Gelegentlich als „Hintertür"-II-V (*backdoor*) bezeichnet, bietet diese Folge eine häufig verwendete und elegante Möglichkeit, um auf die I zurückzukommen. Dabei wird IVm oft ausgelassen und man spielt lediglich I-bVII-I.

6. Rollins liked playing playful, diatonic-type lines, sometimes in a different key. In ms 22, a diatonic line is stated in C, played up a half step in C#, then back down again in C. This is one logical and musical way of "sidestepping" chromatically from one key to another.

6. Rollins mochte spielerische diatonische Linien, die er manchmal in kontrastierenden Tonarten verwendete. In T. 22 wird eine diatonische Linie in C vorgestellt, einen Halbtonschritt höher in C#-Dur wiederholt, und danach wieder in C gespielt: eine logische und musikalische Möglichkeit, sich von einer zur anderen Tonart chromatisch zu bewegen.

Portrait of Charlie Parker, Three Deuces, New York, N.Y., ca. Aug. 1947

10. Bird

Jim Snidero

Slower: ♩ = 92
Faster: ♩ = 135

© 2021 advance music GmbH, Mainz

*) EN = enclosed note / umspielter Ton GT = guide tone PT = passing tone / Durchgangston LT = leading tone / Leitton / Annäherung

Bird

With this final study, we arrive at Charlie "Bird" Parker, arguably the most influential improvisor of the 20th century. Sonny Rollins called Bird the "prophet" of his generation. Without question, Bird was a true genius, revolutionizing jazz and influencing virtually every other genre of music.

Bird's rhythm was, as Dizzy put it, "from another planet", twisting phrases and rhythms in new ways. His sense of melody was unmatched (e. g. *Just Friends* from *Bird With Strings*), and harmonic sophistication among the most advanced of his time. As a saxophonist, Bird possessed incredible technique, a profound tone, and very complex phrasing and articulation. George Coleman once told me that if all the great saxophonists sat at a table, Bird would be on one side, everyone else on the other side. Taken as a whole, Bird was probably the best saxophonist ever.

After his death at the young age of 35, "Bird lives" was seen painted on walls around New York. To this day, that remains true, and is unlikely to change. To ignore Charlie Parker as a jazz musician would be akin to ignoring Bach as a classical composer. There's just too much to learn and build upon.

Bird is based on the AABA form of the Gershwin tune *I Got Rhythm*, which along with the blues, was one of the most common vehicles for bebop improvisation, usually played at a fast tempo. The chord changes to this tune are referred to as "Rhythm Changes", which Bird used as the basis for his tunes *Anthropology, Thriving On A Riff* and *Celebrity*, among others. The usual key for rhythm changes is concert B♭, though there are tunes in other keys as well. This study has two choruses in concert B♭, then modulates to one chorus of concert E♭.

1. As mentioned in *Freddie*, at fast tempos it helps to feel the time 'in 2' (beats 1 and 3) or even whole measures (beat 1). This is the fastest tempo in the book, and requires the most technique. Bird tended to not leave long spaces at fast tempos, and often played longer streams of eighth notes, so the technical challenges on this one keep coming. Refer back to *Freddie* for more on fast tempos.
2. Beyond tempo, rhythm changes themselves can be challenging, as there are a lot of chords. The good news is that, on the A sections, all of the chords function in B♭. That means that it's possible to play B♭ diatonic-type melodies and riffs throughout the entire A section, which are usually less challenging technically than playing the changes.
3. When playing diatonic-type melodies on the A section, there are really only two measures that a line might need to be adjusted from the key of B♭ major; measure 5 with the A adjusted to A♭ to accommodate the B♭7, and measure 6, with the D adjusted to D♭ to accommodate the

Bird

Mit dieser Etüde kommen wir zu Charlie „Bird" Parker, dem wohl einflussreichsten Improvisator des 20. Jahrhunderts. Sonny Rollins nannte Bird den „Propheten" seiner Generation. Bird war ohne Frage ein wahres Genie, das den Jazz revolutionierte und Einfluss auf fast alle anderen Musik-Genres ausübte.

In Dizzys Worten war Birds Rhythmusgefühl „vom anderen Stern": Er drehte Phrasen und Rhythmen auf innovative Art und Weise. Sein Sinn für Melodik war unübertroffen (siehe dazu z. B. *Just Friends* auf *Bird With Strings*) und seine harmonische Raffinesse für die damalige Zeit ausgesprochen avanciert. Auf dem Saxophon war Bird technisch enorm versiert und spielte mit einem tiefgehenden Klang und höchst komplexer Phrasierung und Artikulation. George Coleman hat mir einmal gesagt, wenn alle Saxophongrößen an einem Tisch säßen, befände sich Bird auf der einen Seite und alle anderen auf der gegenüberliegenden Seite. Alles in allem war Bird vermutlich der beste Saxophonist aller Zeiten.

Nach seinem frühzeitigen Tod mit 35 Jahren hat man den Spruch „Bird lives" (Bird lebt) an vielen Wänden in New York aufgemalt. Der Spruch stimmt heute noch immer und bleibt wohl für alle Zeiten bestehen. Sollte man einmal Charlie Parker als Jazzmusiker ignorieren, wäre es so, als wenn man Bach als klassischen Komponisten ignorierte. Es gibt immer noch so viel, was man von ihm lernen und weiterentwickeln kann.

Bird basiert auf der AABA-Form der Gershwin-Melodie *I Got Rhythm*, die neben der Blues-Form eine der häufigsten Grundlagen für Bebop-Improvisation ist und meistens im schnellen Tempo gespielt wird. Die Akkordfolge dieser Melodie wird als „Rhythm Changes" bezeichnet; Bird verwendete sie als Basis unter anderem für seine Melodien *Anthropology, Thriving On A Riff* und *Celebrity*. Die übliche Tonart für Rhythm Changes ist klingend B♭-Dur, auch wenn es Melodien in anderen Tonarten gibt. Diese Etüde enthält zwei Choruse in klingend B♭-Dur, bevor sie für einen weiteren Chorus nach E♭-Dur moduliert.

1. Wie in *Freddie* erwähnt, ist es eine große Hilfe, schnelle Tempi entweder „in 2" (in Halben) oder sogar ganztaktig zu fühlen. Diese Etüde hat das schnellste Tempo im ganzen Heft und erfordert ein Höchstmaß an Technik. Bei schnelleren Stücken pflegte Bird keine großen Pausen einzulegen und spielte stattdessen oft längere Achtelketten, deshalb ist diese Etüde mit vielen technischen Herausforderungen gespickt. Für mehr Information über das schnelle Spielen, schauen Sie beim Stück *Freddie* noch einmal nach.
2. Auch wenn man das Tempo außer Acht lässt, können Rhythm Changes allein wegen der vielen Akkorde eine anspruchsvolle Aufgabe sein. Auf der positiven Seite funktionieren alle Akkorde in den A-Teilen in B♭: Man

Eb7. That's basically what's going on in ms 1–6, but a purely diatonic melody adjusting just A♭ and D♭ could look like this;

kann also während der gesamten A-Teile bei diatonischen Melodien und Riffs auf B♭ bleiben, die eine etwas kleinere technische Herausforderung sind als das Ausspielen der Akkorde.

3. Wenn diatonische Melodien in den A-Teilen gespielt werden, müsste man lediglich jeweils in zwei Takten von B♭-Dur abweichen: In T. 5 müsste das A zu A♭ (für B♭7) und in T. 6 auch das D zu D♭ (für E♭7) abgeändert werden. Genau das kann man in T. 1–6 beobachten. Eine durchgehende diatonische Melodie nur mit Änderung der beiden Noten A♭ und D♭ könnte dagegen wie folgt aussehen:

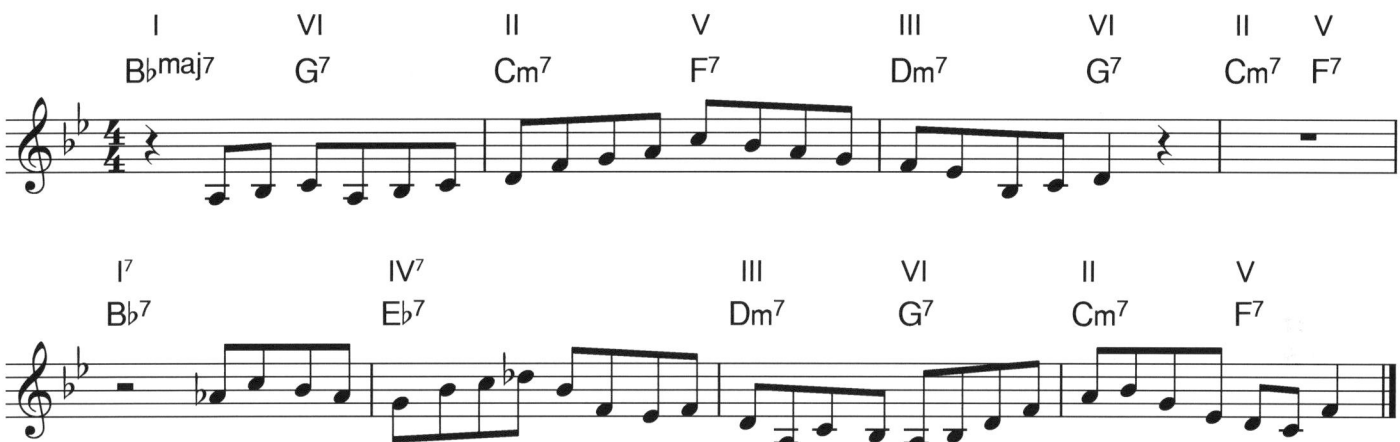

4. Though it's possible to play diatonically throughout every A section, that would probably sound a bit boring. On *Amazing Bud*, we saw that diatonic ideas were used on the first two measures of the A section, followed by two measures of changes, and that is typical on rhythm changes as well (ms 33–36, 41–45, 73–76). Again, it's about finding a good balance between melodic approaches.

5. An especially important point with this etude is the way that lines compliment each other, creating a sense of ebb and flow that keeps things interesting. For example, the line from ms 5–10 is within a relatively tight range of about an octave, concentrating on harmonic substitutions to create interest. The next line goes much higher and has a wider range with just one substitution (ms 15, E♭m over B♭ major) creating an attractive contrast to the previous line.

6. As mentioned, Bird had an incredible sense of rhythm. This not only refers to rhythmic ideas (ms 37–38), but also to asymmetrical phrasing and the illusion of shifting meters (see *Monktified*).
    - ms 9–10; creates hemiola using note groupings that imply 3/4 over 4/4
    - ms 13, 61, 63, 77; lines delay the resolution to beat 3
    - ms 25; beats 1 and 2 imply a diminished chord, delaying the resolution to imply beat 1 on beat 3
    - ms 29–31; once again, creates hemiola using note groupings that imply 3/4 over 4/4
    - ms 41–42; places melody stated 8 ms earlier on beat 3, implying shifting meter

4. Auch wenn man in jedem A-Teil durchgehend diatonische Melodien spielen könnte, würde das ziemlich langweilig klingen. In *Amazing Bud* haben wir beobachtet, wie man diatonische Ideen jeweils für die ersten beiden Takte einsetzen kann, gefolgt von zwei Takten mit akkordbasierten Linien. Das gleiche Prinzip ist auch für Rhythm Changes durchaus typisch (T. 33–36, 41–45, 73–76). Auch hier geht es wieder darum, eine gute Balance zwischen verschiedenen Arten von Melodieführungen zu finden.

5. Ein wichtiger Aspekt dieser Etüde ist die Art, wie sich die verschiedenen Linien ergänzen und ein abwechslungsreiches, fließendes Spielen entsteht. Die Linie in T. 5–10 zum Beispiel bleibt innerhalb des relativ engen Umfangs einer Oktave, indem die Spannung durch harmonische Substitutionen erzeugt wird. Die darauffolgende Linie geht mit einem größeren Umfang viel höher, enthält aber nur eine einzige Substitution (T. 15, E♭m über B♭-Dur) und stellt einen starken Kontrast zur vorherigen Linie dar.

6. Wie schon erwähnt, hatte Bird einen unglaublichen Sinn für Rhythmus, nicht nur in seinen rhythmischen Ideen T. 37–38), sondern auch im Sinne von asymmetrischer Phrasierung und der Illusion eines verschobenen Zeitmaßes (siehe *Monktified*).
    - T. 9–10: Durch das Gruppieren von Noten, die einen 3/4-Takt über dem 4/4-Takt suggerieren, werden Hemiolen erzeugt.
    - T. 13, 61, 63, 77: Hier wird die Auflösung auf den dritten Schlag verschoben.

- ms 71, 89; the ultimate resolution is delayed to beat 4
- ms 84–86; places line on beat 4 instead of 3, implying shifting meter

All of these examples help the music to float over the time, abstracting beat 1. Combine melodic ebb and flow and harmonic variety with rhythmic abstraction, and you have a very interesting solo.

7. The basic changes on the bridge are two measures each of III7, VI7, II7, V7 (D^7, G^7, C^7, F^7). But as is the case here, the related minor II chord is often placed in the first measure of each 2-measure change (Am^7-D^7, Dm^7-G^7, Gm^7-C^7, Cm^7-F^7). The bridge is a good place to use dominant bebop scales, as well as added half steps to those scales, as mentioned in *Miles '63* and *Freddie*.

8. One interesting harmonic concept Bird would use is to play a chord substitution first, then the normal chord second (it's usually the other way around). In ms 17 the tritone substitute A♭^{7} is implied over a D^7. In the following measure the line goes back to D^7. This also happens on *Bird And Diz* in ms 53–54, first using ♯11, then natural 11.

9. A diminished idea can be used virtually anywhere on the A section (ms 29–31), helping the line to float by suspending the harmony. Here it's at the end of an A section, but it would work just as well at the beginning of an A section.

10. In ms 41–42, a classic 'Bird' idea that was stated in ms 33–34 is played up a minor third, the key of D♭. This can sound good, and works well harmonically since the same notes are contained in IVm (E♭m^7), which lead smoothly back to I.

11. Bird was fond of introduced humor by quoting melodies from other tunes. He loved Stravinsky, and sometimes quoted *Petrushka*, (ms 72–74), but again, it's about timing, with this diatonic melody placed at the beginning of an A section.

- T. 25: Auf dem ersten und zweiten Schlag wird ein verminderter Akkord angedeutet, dessen Auflösung auf Schlag 3 die Takteins suggeriert.
- T. 29–31: Hier werden wiederum Hemiolen geschaffen durch die Andeutung eines 3/4-Taktes über dem 4/4-Takt.
- T. 41–42: An dieser Stelle wird die Melodie von vor 8 Takten auf dem dritten Schlag wiederholt, wodurch der Eindruck eines verschobenen Zeitmaßes entsteht.
- T. 71, 89: Die letzte Auflösung wird auf Schlag 4 verschoben.
- T. 84–86: Die Linie wird auf dem vierten anstelle des dritten Schlags platziert, was wiederum die Illusion des verschobenen Zeitmaßes erzeugt.

All diese Techniken lassen die Musik quasi über dem Zeitmaß schweben und abstrahieren den Schlag 1. Wenn Sie die melodische Dichte und eine variantenreiche Harmonik mit rhythmischer Abstraktion kombinieren, können Sie ein sehr interessantes Solo vorlegen.

7. Die Bridge besteht im Wesentlichen aus der Akkordfolge III7-VI7-II7-V7 (D^7, G^7, C^7, F^7), wobei jeder Akkord zwei Takte lang gehalten wird. Einer gängigen Abwandlung folgend wird auch hier der zugehörige II-Mollakkord im jeweils ersten Takt eingeschoben, sodass die Akkordfolge Am^7-D^7, Dm^7-G^7, Gm^7-C^7, Cm^7-F^7 entsteht. Dominant-Bebopskalen eignen sich vorzüglich für die Bridge, auch mit den bei *Miles '63* und *Freddie* erwähnten zusätzlichen Halbtonschritten.

8. Eines von Birds interessanten harmonischen Konzepten bestand darin, die Akkordsubstitution vor dem normalen Akkord zu spielen (üblicherweise wird umgekehrt verfahren). In T. 17 wird die Tritonussubstitution A♭^{7} über einem D^7-Akkord impliziert. Im folgenden Takt kehrt die Linie zu D^7 zurück. Dasselbe kann man in T. 53–54 in *Bird And Diz* beobachten, zunächst mit einer ♯11 und danach mit einer 11.

9. Eine verminderte Idee kann fast überall in den A-Teilen gespielt werden (T. 29–31): Weil sie einen Vorhalt impliziert, erzeugt sie einen schwebenden Klang. In dieser Etüde erscheint der verminderte Sound am Ende des A-Teils, es wäre aber am Anfang des Abschnitts genau so wirkungsvoll.

10. In T. 41–42 sehen wir eine klassische Idee von Bird, die in T. 33–34 der Etüde vorgestellt wurde, und hier nun eine kleine Terz höher in D♭-Dur erscheint. Dieser schöne Effekt passt auch in Bezug auf die Harmonik, da die gleichen Noten auch in dem Akkord IVm (E♭m^7) enthalten sind, der auf direktem Wege zur I zurückführt.

11. Bird hatte auch seine Freude an humorvollen Melodien, die aus bekannten Werken stammten. Er liebte Strawinsky und zitierte hin und wieder *Petrushka* (T. 72–74); die diatonische Melodie wird hier am Anfang eines A-Teils platziert und fügt sich stimmig ein.

Appendix | Anhang

Interview: Ken Peplowski On Studying With Sonny Stitt

Growing up near Cleveland, the great tenor saxophonist and clarinetist Ken Peplowski (see clarinet edition) was able to hear and study with saxophonist Sonny Stitt when visiting the area. Stitt was one of the greatest saxophonists ever, possessing incredible technique and precision, and a major influence on many historically significant saxophonists including John Coltrane and George Coleman.

Jim You saw Sonny Stitt play about a dozen times. What were some of his favorite tunes?

Ken He'd always play a blues and rhythm changes, maybe *Cherokee* and *Lover Man*. But he had such a great repertoire that he would surprise you with tunes, too. I once showed him a book of a 1001 tunes during a lesson, and he looked through the table of contents and played the melody to many of them. Not always in the standard key, either. Just what felt right to him at that time.

Jim I heard that he could play any tune in any key. Melody, chords, everything.

Ken I think that may be true. He had the best sense of relative pitch I've ever heard, the relationship between the notes and the chords. It was just in his head. When we would have a lesson, he didn't talk about the number system [editor's note: e. g. II-V-I], or articulate theory. Instead, he would play things at me, and I could hear the II-V-I, diminished chords, whatever. He just had the sound in his head, the arc of phrases and how everything related to each other.

Jim George Coleman told me Stitt was a real technician on the horn. He knew everything about the saxophone. What did you work on in lessons in that regard?

Ken Well, one thing was breathing. That you had to breath from down here (*points to stomach, diaphragm*) pushing the air through, but that everything went into it, from the bottom of your toes to the top of your head! He said you had to project the sound, play to the back of the room, and he had that beautiful, singing sound on both instruments. But he would also talk in philosophical term, that everything you do is music and goes into what you're playing.

Jim On a funny note, one of his trick questions was how many keys are there on the saxophone.

Ken That's right! And no matter what you said, the answer was wrong!

Jim Any discussion about performing?

Interview mit Ken Peplowski über das Studium bei Sonny Stitt

Der große Tenorsaxofonist und Klarinettist Ken Peplowski (siehe Ausgabe für Klarinette) ist in der Nähe von Cleveland aufgewachsen. Er bekam die Möglichkeit, den Saxophonisten Sonny Stitt beim Spielen zu erleben und bei ihm zu studieren, wenn dieser sich in der Gegend aufhielt. Stitt war einer der allzeit Größten unter den Saxophonisten mit einer unglaublichen Technik und Präzision und übte einen maßgeblichen Einfluss auf viele historisch bedeutende Saxophonisten aus, darunter John Coltrane und George Coleman.

Jim Du hast Sony Stitt mindestens ein Dutzend Mal spielen sehen. Was waren seine Lieblingsmelodien?

Ken Er spielte immer einen Blues und Rhythm Changes, vielleicht auch *Cherokee* oder *Lover Man*. Er hatte aber ein so umfangreiches Repertoire, dass er einem immer wieder überraschen konnte. Während einer Unterrichtsstunde habe ich ihm einmal ein Heft mit 1001 Melodien gezeigt: Er schaute sich das Inhaltsverzeichnis an und spielte spontan viele der Melodien. Nicht immer in der Originaltonart, sondern wie es ihm gerade in dem Augenblick passte.

Jim Ich hörte, er könne jedes Stück in allen Tonarten spielen: Melodie, Akkorde und einfach alles.

Ken Ich glaube, die Geschichte stimmt. Er hatte das beste relative Gehör, das ich je beobachtet habe – die Beziehungen zwischen den Tönen und Akkorden. Alles hatte er einfach im Kopf. Als ich Unterricht bei ihm nahm, erwähnte er nichts über die Akkordbezifferung [Anm. d. Red.: z. B. II-V-I] oder Theorie. Stattdessen spielte er mir was vor und ich erkannte sofort II-V-I-Verbindungen, verminderte Akkorde und alles Mögliche noch dazu. Er hatte den Klang einfach im Kopf, den Spannungsbogen eines Solos und wie alles miteinander verbunden war.

Jim George Coleman sagte mir, Stitt sei ein großer Techniker auf dem Horn gewesen. Er wusste alles über das Saxophon. Inwiefern spielte das im Unterricht eine Rolle?

Ken Also, Atmung war ein Hauptanliegen: Dass man von hier unten (*zeigt auf Bauch, Zwerchfell*) atmen müsse, um die Luft durchzupusten, aber dass immer der ganze Körper, von der Fußsohle bis zum Kopf, im Einsatz war! Er sagte, man müsse den Klang bis hinten in den Raum projizieren, dabei spielte er mit einem wunderbaren gesanglichen Timbre auf beiden Instrumenten. Er redete aber außerdem über den philosophischen Aspekt, dass alles, was man mache, mit Musik zu tun habe und in das gerade Gespielte fließen würde.

Ken	The funny thing is that I find myself playing with local rhythm sections these days, and of course he did that all the time. He would talk about the discipline of playing with three strangers, and if you could hook up with one of them, you learned to block the other two out. And if you can't hook up with anyone, you play for yourself. He grew so strong doing this, and I heard him lift a rhythm section with his incredible time.	**Jim**	Eine lustige Sache war einer seiner Trickfragen: "How many keys are there on the saxophone?". [Anm. d. Red.: Ein Wortspiel auf das Wort ‚key', dt. Klappe oder Tonart]
Jim	Did Stitt show you any exercises?	**Ken**	Ja, das stimmt! Und egal, was man als Antwort gab, es war immer falsch!
Ken	He did, but is was mostly playing things, and I'd play them back. He once wrote something out, kind of II-V-I exercises, and I think that era of players was based around that whole thing, II-V-Is, and you hear that in a lot of the American song book from that era.	**Jim**	Gab es Erläuterungen zum Vorspielen?
		Ken	Das Lustige ist, dass ich heutzutage oft mit verschiedenen örtlichen Rhythmusgruppen auftrete: Das hat er die ganze Zeit getan. Er redete von der Disziplin, mit drei Fremden zu spielen, sich auf einen zu orientieren, während man die anderen zwei ausblendet. Wenn es unmöglich sei, mit irgendeinem der drei zusammenzuspielen, spiele man eben für sich alleine. Dadurch gewann er an Stärke und ich hörte, wie er eine ganze Rhythmusgruppe mit seinem unglaublichen Zeitgefühl mitziehen konnte.
Jim	I studied with Phil Woods, and he once told me that 75% of jazz was II-V-I.	**Jim**	Hat Stitt dir irgendwelche Übungen auch gezeigt?
Ken	Yeah, at least that kind of jazz. I took a couple of lessons with Phil, and it was that kind of thing. Phil would spell it out, articulate it, Stitt would say "try this", and play it at me.	**Ken**	Ja, hat er, es ging aber hauptsächlich so, dass er mir was vorspielte und ich es nachspielte. Einmal hat er etwas aufgeschrieben, eine Art II-V-I-Übung, und ich glaube, die II-V-I-Konzepte waren für Musiker in dieser Zeit einfach das A und O – man hört sehr viele davon im American Songbook dieser Epoche.
Jim	Anything else you'd like to add about Stitt?	**Jim**	Ich habe mit Phil Woods studiert, der mir einmal erzählte, 75 % von Jazz sei auf II-V-I aufgebaut.
Ken	Man, he had an unerring sense of what a song was, the changes, the arc of the song. I just felt that, of all the saxophonists, he was so consistent through lots of situations, and that he always produced at a certain level. It was amazing.	**Ken**	Ja, auf jeden Fall diese Art von Jazz. Ich habe einige Stunden bei Phil genommen, und es drehte sich alles um dieses Thema. Phil hat alles buchstabiert und artikuliert, während Stitt sagte, „probiere es so", und mir das einfach vorspielte.
		Jim	Hast du noch etwas über Stitt zu erzählen?
		Ken	O Mann, er hatte ein treffsicheres Gespür für Songs: die Akkordfolgen, den Aufbau. Ich spürte einfach, dass er von allen Saxophonisten in vielen Situationen immer konsequent blieb, und zu allen Zeiten ein bestimmtes Niveau behielt. Er war einfach großartig.

Suggested Reading | Literaturempfehlungen

- Gary Giddins: *Celebrating Bird* (Beech Tree)
- Dizzy Gillespie with Al Fraser: *To Be Or Not To Bop* (Da Capo)
- Miles Davis with Quiney Troupe: *Miles* (Simon and Schuster)
- J.C Thomas: *Chasin' The Trane* (Da Capo)
- Ralph Gleason: *Conversations In Jazz* (Yale University Press)
- Richard Cook: *Blue Note Records: The Biography* (Justin, Charles and Company)

Suggested Listening & Videos | Hörempfehlungen und Videos

Monktified
- *Thelonious Monk Trio* (Prestige)
- Thelonious Monk Quartet, *Live at Carnegie Hall* (Blue Note)
- Thelonious Monk, *Blue Monk* (YouTube video)

The Messengers
- Art Blakey and the Jazz Messengers, *Moanin'* (Blue Note)
- Bobby Timmons, *Moanin'* (Riverside)
- *The Jazz Messengers Live, Belgium 1958* (YouTube video)

Amazing Bud
- Bud Powell, *The Amazing Bud Powell* (Blue Note)
- Hank Mobley, *Mobley's Message* (Prestige)
- *The Jazz Messengers Live, Paris 1959* (YouTube video)

Pure Silver
- Horace Silver, *Horace-Scope* (Blue Note)
- Chet Baker, *Live In London Vol. 2* (Ubuntu)
- Louis Hayes, *Serenade for Horace* (Blue Note)

Miles '63
- Miles Davis, *Miles In Europe* (Columbia)
- Miles Davis, *'Round about Midnight* (Columbia)
- Miles Davis, *My Funny Valentine* (Columbia)

Bird And Diz
- Dizzy Gillespie, *Hot House* (Guild)
- *Jazz at Massey Hall* (Debut Records)
- Charlie Parker and Dizzy Gillespie, *Hot House* (YouTube video)

Straight Trane
- John Coltrane, *Coltrane* (Prestige)
- Kenny Garrett, *African Exchange Student* (Atlantic)
- Eric Alexander, *Solid* (Milestone)

Freddie
- Freddie Hubbard, *Ready For Freddie* (Birdlike)
- Freddie Hubbard, *Birdlike 1967* (YouTube video)
- Freddie Hubbard, *Birdlike, Mt Fuji* (YouTube video)

One For Sonny
- Sonny Rollins, *A Night At The Village Vanguard* (Blue Note)
- Charlie Parker, *The Complete Master Takes* (Verve)
- *Nancy Wilson/Cannonball Adderley* (Capitol)

Bird
- Charlie Parker, *Thriving On A Riff* (Savoy)
- Charlie Parker And The All-Stars Live, *Summit Meeting At Birdland* (Columbia)
- Charlie Parker, *Celebrity* (YouTube video)

About The Author And The Musicians

Jim Snidero is an alto saxophonist and composer based in New York. He has over 50 solo and sideman recordings for EMI, Milestone and Savant, among others, and has been included in both Downbeat Magazine's critics and readers polls. Snidero is also a best-selling author ("Jazz Conception"/Advance Music), was a visiting professor at Indiana U and Princeton, and is on the faculty at New School Jazz and Contemporary Music. Snidero plays Selmer saxophones and D'Addario reeds. Learn more at www.jimsnidero.com.

Musicians

Originally from Sweden, **Anders Bostrom** studied at Berklee College of Music, then moved to New York in 1991, where he has been a prominent jazz voice on flute, recording with Walt Weiskopf and Donny McCaslin, among many. Bostrom is regularly heard on NY Broadway shows including *The Lion King*, *Tarzan*, and *Bombay Dreams*.

Mike LeDonne is one of the only musicians in jazz history to be a true master of both the piano and organ (Downbeat critics poll). LeDonne has dozens of recordings on both instruments as a soloist, and appears on over 60 recordings as a sideman. He has been the pianist with historic jazz artists Sonny Rollins, Milt Jackson, Benny Golson, Ron Carter, George Coleman, among many others, and taught at Juilliard's Jazz @ Lincoln Center.

Bassist **Peter Washington** has recorded more than any other bassist of his generation, with over 400 recordings to his credit. Since moving to New York and being a member of Art Blakey's Jazz Messengers in the early 1980's, Washington has worked with countless jazz greats including Dizzy Gillespie, Freddie Hubbard, Cedar Walton, and Jackie McLean. He was a long-time member of jazz giant Tommy Flanagan's piano trio.

With over 100 recordings to his credit, **Joe Farnsworth** is one of the most in-demand drummers on the New York jazz scene. He has held the drum chair in some of the best piano trios in history, including McCoy Tyner, Cedar Walton and Horace Silver, was a member of Pharoah Sander's group, and worked with Johnny Griffin, George Coleman, and Lou Donaldson, among others. He is a founding member of the One for All Sextet.

Über den Autor und die Musiker

Der Altsaxophonist und Komponist **Jim Snidero** lebt in New York. Er hat mehr als 50 Aufnahmen als Solist und Sideman für EMI, Milestone, Savant und andere Labels aufgenommen und wurde mit dem Critics' Poll und Readers' Poll der Fachzeitschrift Downbeat ausgezeichnet. Snidero ist Bestsellerautor („Jazz Conception"/Advance Music), war Gastprofessor an der Indiana Universität und in Princeton und ist Mitglied der Fakultät der New School Jazz and Contemporary Music. Snidero spielt Saxophone von Selmer und benutzt Blätter von D'Addario. Weitere Infos unter www.jimsnidero.com.

Musiker

Der gebürtige Schwede **Anders Bostrom** hat am Berklee College of Music studiert und ist 1991 nach New York gezogen, wo er seitdem eine prominente Jazzstimme auf der Flöte ist. Er hat u.a. mit Walt Weiskopf und Donny McCaslin Aufnahmen eingespielt. Bostrom ist regelmäßig in Shows am New Yorker Broadway zu hören, darunter *The Lion King*, *Tarzan* und *Bombay Dreams*.

Mike LeDonne ist einer der wenigen Musiker der Jazzgeschichte, der gleichzeitig ein Meister des Klaviers als auch der Orgel ist (Downbeat Critics Poll). Er hat Dutzende CDs als Solist gemacht und ist als Sideman bei über 60 Aufnahmen dabei. Als Pianist hat er mit historischen Jazz-Artists wie Sonny Rollins, Milt Jackson, Benny Golson, Ron Carter, George Coleman und vielen anderen gespielt und am Juilliard's Jazz im Lincoln Center gelehrt.

Der Kontrabassist **Peter Washington** hat mehr Aufnahmen als jeder andere Bassist seiner Generation gemacht – an über 400 Aufnahmen ist er bislang beteiligt! Seit seinem Umzug nach New York und seiner Mitgliedschaft bei Art Blakey's Jazz Messengers in den frühen 80er Jahren hat Washington mit unzähligen Größen des Jazz gearbeitet, darunter Dizzy Gillespie, Freddie Hubbard, Cedar Walton und Jackie McLean. Er war außerdem für lange Zeit Mitglied des Klaviertrios von Jazz-Koryphäe Tommy Flanagan.

Mit mehr als 100 Aufnahmen ist **Joe Farnsworth** einer der meistgefragten Schlagzeuger der New Yorker Jazzszene. Er war fester Schlagzeuger in einigen der besten Klaviertrios der Geschichte, u.a. bei McCoy Tyner, Cedar Walton und Horace Silver, war Mitglied der Band um Pharoah Sander und arbeitete mit Johnny Griffin, George Coleman, Lou Donaldson und vielen anderen Musikern zusammen. Er ist Gründungsmitglied des One for All Sextet.